D0290584

THE
MOLECULAR BASIS
OF MEMORY

EDWARD M. GUROWITZ, *Ph.D.*

PRENTICE-HALL, Inc., *Englewood Cliffs, New Jersey*

To NANCY and AMY

Copyright ©1969 by PRENTICE-HALL, Inc.
Englewood Cliffs, New Jersey

All rights reserved. No part of this book
may be reproduced in any form or by any means
without permission in writing from the publisher.

Library of Congress Catalog Card Number: 68-57208

PRINTED IN THE UNITED STATES OF AMERICA

Current Printing (last digit):
10 9 8 7 6 5 4 3

Prentice-Hall International, Inc. (*London*)
Prentice-Hall of Australia, Pty. Ltd. (*Sydney*)
Prentice-Hall of Canada, Ltd. (*Toronto*)
Prentice-Hall of India Private Ltd. (*New Delhi*)
Prentice-Hall of Japan, Inc. (*Tokyo*)

PREFACE

In this review I have attempted to bring together evidence on the nature of memory from a variety of disparate sources, including psychology, neurology, biochemistry, and others. The area of study which concerns itself with the chemical or molecular basis of memory is a relatively new one, and is still very much in progress; much work, for example, has been published during the interval between completion of the manuscript in January, 1968, and the time of this writing. I have, however, attempted to review critically the work done up until this time, and to form some theoretical framework of the apparently chaotic mass of data.

This book is written for use both by students of psychology and of other disciplines at the undergraduate level and beyond. As such, it presupposes only a minimal knowledge of the principles of conditioning and learning as can be obtained from any good introductory psychology text. A chapter on the basic biochemical principles involved in this work is included for those readers whose background in this area may be weak. It is my hope that this chapter might serve double duty as a ready reference for structural formulas, etc., for all readers.

The author finds himself indebted to far more people than can be acknowledged. In certain cases, however, the extent of this indebtedness is so great that mention must be made. I am, first of all, most grateful to James Ison for his guidance and for his many critical readings of the manuscript. The suggestions of Michael Davidson and Lowell Glasgow are also appreciated. Mention must also be made of the help and support I received from David Gross and from my brother, William Gurowitz. Much of the final writing of this book was done during the course of an NIMH postdoctoral traineeship at the University of Illinois College of Medicine, and I am grateful to Arthur Kling for his assistance during this time.

I further wish to acknowledge the kindness of the following journals and publishers for their permission to quote from various articles and books: John Wiley and Sons, Blackwell Scientific Publications, *Psychopharmacologia, Science, The Psychonomic Press, Texas Reports in Biology and Medicine, Comparative Psychology Monographs, International Journal of Neuropsychiatry,* and *Proceedings of the National Academy of Sciences.*

iii

CONTENTS

	INTRODUCTION	1
I	EVIDENCE FOR A CHEMICAL BASIS FOR LEARNING AND MEMORY	3
II	THE NATURE OF THE MEMORY MOLECULE	9
III	BASIC CHEMICAL CONSIDERATIONS	13
IV	DNA AS THE MEMORY MOLECULE	23
V	RNA AS THE MEMORY MOLECULE	25
VI	PROTEIN AS THE MEMORY MOLECULE	49
VII	STUDIES OF INTER-ANIMAL TRANSFER OF LEARNING	59
VIII	CONCLUSION	77
	REFERENCES	79
	INDEX	89

INTRODUCTION

Psychologists have long been interested in the problems of learning, memory, and recall, or as they have sometimes been called in recent years, information encoding, storage, and retrieval. A variety of theories have been proposed as to how information is stored in the nervous system and most of these, until recently, held that some sort of structural neural alteration took place in the brain. More recently, however, a new type of theory has come into prominence which gives changes in brain chemistry a central role in memory storage. Such chemical theories have found much supportive evidence in the research of the past decade, especially that of the past five years.

This review will trace the various strands of evidence on the chemical basis of memory and learning, and will attempt to draw some conclusions from the often contradictory data. The organization of the review will be as follows. In Chapter I, the evidence which led to the view that memory might have a chemical basis will be reviewed, and arguments will be presented to support the view that memory has two components based on its time course, and that one of these, namely, long-term memory, is chemical in nature.

The form that this chemical basis might take and the criteria for evaluating possible candidates for the role of memory substrate will be discussed in Chapter II. Chapter III constitutes a review of basic biochemical concepts and mechanisms which might be involved in memory.

Current evidence for the chemical basis of memory and learning has come mainly from two sources. In the first, the experimenter attempts to alter the metabolism of a suspected memory substrate and then tests for the effects of

1

this intervention on learning or memory. Another related procedure involves first training subjects on a task and then testing for any effects of this training on particular chemicals in the brain. In the second, the experimenter trains animals on a task and then injects the brains of these animals into naïve animals, which are then tested for learning on the same task. In this second procedure the investigator may extract a particular chemical he believes might be the memory substrate, he may remove this chemical, or he may inject an undifferentiated homogenate, subsequently testing this to find the active agent. The first type of study, which is directed toward the delineation of a single possible substrate, will be discussed in Chapters IV, V, and VI for DNA, RNA, and protein respectively. The second type, or inter-animal transfer of learning study, will be reviewed in Chapter VII. I will attempt a synthesis of the work reviewed to provide an overview of the area as a whole in Chapter VIII.

chapter
I

EVIDENCE FOR A CHEMICAL BASIS FOR LEARNING AND MEMORY

The mammalian brain is composed of some billions of nerve cells all more or less alike which, we assume, contribute to behavior and to "mental activity" by their patterns of firing. It is this assumption which underlies the research in the field variously known as neuropsychology psychobiology, physiological psychology, or some equivalent term. In view of this background it is not surprising that the first of the latter-day theories of learning and memory considered these processes to be based in some form of ongoing electrical activity. These theories (*e.g.*, Hebb, 1949; Lashley, 1950) will not be individually reviewed here, but a few of their common characteristics should be noted. Many of these theories attributed the learning process to some sort of neural circuit activated by the association of stimulus and response, generally through their contiguous occurrence. It followed that memory consisted of the maintenance, by some means, of activity in these circuits over time. The theorists then went on to treat problems such as the localization of this circuit or engram, the temporal factors in its establishment and maintenance, and the like, always taking the basic assumption for granted. Beginning in the 1940's, however, this assumption came to be doubted as the result of a series of experimental tests.

Studies Using Electroconvulsive Shock

If learning and memory were dependent upon ongoing neural activity, then it should be possible to disrupt memory by interference with this activity. In 1948, Duncan reported a series of studies using electroconvulsive shock (ECS) as a means of "scrambling" brain electrical activity. The ECS procedure involves the passage of a brief electric current across the brain, usually by means of electrodes attached to the ears or the scalp or either side of the skull. A convulsive seizure, usually followed by unconsciousness, occurs as a result of the shock (Deutsch and Deutsch, 1966). The general paradigm for these studies is as follows. First groups of animals are trained on a simple learning task to some criterion; then, at varying intervals after criterion is attained, the groups receive some treatment, in this case ECS, and finally a retention measure is taken. Duncan administered ECS at intervals from 40 sec. to 14 hr. after each trial of an avoidance problem in which rats were given one trial per day for 18 days. He found that if ECS was given one hour or more after the trial there was no effect on learning, whereas ECS given up to 15 min. after trials did show a deleterious effect.

Thompson and Dean (1955) pointed out that in the procedure used by Duncan the inference that disruption of memory was accomplished is complicated by two factors. First, the 18 daily convulsions may have had a cumulative effect, and second there may have been a punishing effect on animals receiving ECS shortly after the trial. That is, the ECS may have induced aversive properties to the goal box. Thompson and Dean attempted to circumvent these difficulties by use of a massed practice training procedure, again in an avoidance task, followed by a single ECS after the subjects reached criterion. ECS was administered at intervals from 10 sec. to 4 hr., and resulted in an increasing savings function with only the 4 hr. group reaching the savings level of control Ss. It should be noted here that the time intervals within which ECS was effective in Thompson and Dean's study do not agree with those of Duncan or of a further study by Gerard which they cite. Although all three find ECS effective at short intervals, they do not agree on the maximum length of time that may elapse between learning and convulsion. Thompson and Dean attributed this to a number of possible factors, such as number of trials. They interpreted their results, as well as those of Duncan and of Gerard, as evidence for the disruption of perserverative or reverberatory neural activity during an initial short period of fixation. This seems comparable to Müller and Pilzecker's earlier notion of a consolidation phase for memory (Grossman, 1967).

Coons and Miller (1960) also raised the problem of ECS acting as a fear-inducing punishment in the goal box. Thompson and Dean attempted to minimize this problem through the use of only a single ECS. Madsen and McGaugh (1961), by employing a step-down type of passive avoidance response (PAR), succeeded in eliminating this as a source of confounding. In the PAR procedure, the deprived animal is first trained to receive food (or water) at a particular location, and is then shocked while feeding at this location. Given a shock of sufficient intensity, the animal learns (often after a single shock) to avoid the food dish. Thus, a sort of "one-trial learning" is established. The study of Madsen and McGaugh was based on the premise that if ECS interferes with memory then rats should continue to make the response which was punished and followed by ECS. "If, however, ECS affects performance by inducing fear, Ss given an ECS following a response punished by shock should tend *not* to make the punished response on a subsequent test" (p.522). That is, the use of the PAR puts the two possible effects of ECS in opposition in terms of their effect on the animal's performance. Their results, based on 96 subjects, support the memory-interference hypothesis, rather than the fear-induction one.

Chorover and Schiller further investigated the amnesic effects of ECS and the problem of its aversive effects. In their first study (1965), they compared the results of single and repeated ECS, .5-60.0 sec. after single PAR trials. Here they confirmed the earlier findings of an inverse relationship between ECS-delay and memory impairment. Impairment, however, occurred only at the shortest (0.5-10.0 sec.) intervals in contrast to the much longer intervals observed in the earlier studies. In investigating the aversive effects of ECS, they found that these effects did not seem to develop after a single ECS, but seemed to require repeated convulsions. They assert that ECS must be repeated in order to establish a classically conditioned aversive response.

Since successful conditioning presumably requires that S "remember" the CS, it is only when delay interval is increased up to 10 sec. (*i.e.,* to the apparent limits of the [retrograde amnesia] that it becomes possible for the aversive consequences of the ECS to be conditioned to antecedent stimuli in the test situation (p. 77).

Chorover and Schiller thus conclude that ECS induces a *brief* retrograde amnesia (RA), but provide no answer for the problem raised by the lack of accord between their results and those of earlier studies.

In a later study (Chorover and Schiller, 1966), the same authors obtained evidence contradicting these earlier results. In a replication of a study by Bureš and Burešová (1963), to be discussed below, they found that ECS did not induce the short-lasting RA of their 1965 study, but what *appeared* to be a longer-lasting RA. In three subsequent experiments reported in the same paper they presented evidence to indicate that passive avoidance in this type of situation does not necessarily involve learning and retention of a response to a specific set of cues, but rather of a generalized conditioned emotional response (CER) to the whole experimental situation. This CER results in decreased locomotion ("freezing"), which facilitates PAR performance. ECS, Chorover and Schiller feel, somehow disinhibits the animal and normal exploratory behavior manifests itself as a PAR deficit. The evidence they present for this view is that the Bureš technique, which uses confinement training, capitalizes on the fact that exploratory activity is suppressed during confinement training and that ECS reduces this suppression. Furthermore

When the CER-inducing procedure...is replaced by... [a] paradigm that allows escape from foot shock,... convulsed animals no longer manifest the long-term disruptive effect (p.40).

These considerations, along with their previous (1965) finding that a step-down PAR yields only a brief RA, led Chorover and Schiller to the conclusion that much of the long-term amnesic effect of ECS is due to motor disinhibition. It is important for our purposes to note that these authors do not reject the notion that ECS interferes with memory but propose that ECS-induced RA is only of very brief duration: "...the period required for initiating the structural encoding of memory traces probably does not exceed a few seconds" (p.41). Whether this is the case is open to debate, as we shall see. What is most important about this evidence, however, is that it seems to clearly establish that insofar as the ECS data are concerned there is a period, of as yet indeterminate length, immediately following learning when memory encoding is liable to attack by the disruption of brain electrical activity. Perhaps of more relevance to the problem of this review is the fact that after this period, ECS-produced interference with the presumed electrical activity has *no* effect on memory.

Studies Using Other Means of Disrupting Memory

Other means than ECS have been used to disrupt brain electrical activity. Gerard (1953) and Andjus *et al.* (1956) investigated both anterograde and retrograde effects of severe hypothermia in rats. In the latter study it was found that cooling rats down to $0°$ to $1°C$ severely impaired subsequent learning of a maze problem. Hypothermia at this level results in complete arrest of heart beat, circulation, and respiration, with cerebral activity arrested for some 2 hours or more. Although they do not indicate the intervals they used, they state that the impairment was greatest at the shortest intervals between cooling and training (less than 2 hours). Retrograde effects, *i.e.*, the effects on retention, are not so clear in this study. Although there was no significant effect of cooling on retention the authors emphasized a strong trend in this direction and concluded that their results are difficult to explain if it is assumed that long term memory is dependent upon continuous brain activity. It should be noted that this work was done with rats which are homoiothermic, nonhibernating animals, whose systems are not well suited to the methods of cryobiology. Gerard (1963) cited similar work done with hamsters, which *are* hibernators, which indicates again that interference with brain electrical activity is not adequate to disrupt long-term or well-established memory.

In 1961, Pearlman, Sharpless, and Jarvik investigated the amnesic effects of convulsions induced by the drug pentylenetetrazol (Metrazol), and of anesthesia induced either by ether or by intravenous administration of sodium pentabarbitol. The learning task was one in which *S*s were first trained to bar press for water and then given a single electric shock through the bar which results in suppression of the bar press. This was taken as demonstration of a conditioned emotional response. They found that "surgical anesthesia severely impaired the retention...if induced within 10 to 15 min. after the learning trial" (p.111). Not only was the Metrazol convulsion effective in abolishing the response up to 8 hr., but it also depressed the response even after 4 days. These authors felt that the impairment which occurred hours or days after the learning trial was probably induced in some way different from that which occurs shortly after learning. They drew an analogy between this situation and that of post-convulsive human patients who often show temporary memory derangement.

Cortical spreading depression (CSD) has also been used to attempt to disrupt memory. The first major study on this was that of Bureš and Burešová (1963), which compared the effects of ECS and CSD, both given at 1 min. or 2 hr. after learning either a reversal of a left-right discrimination or of a PAR. In both cases both ECS and CSD disrupted the new memory at both time intervals. ECS always had the greater effect, and the effect of both treatments at 2 hr. was much weaker than at 1 min. We have already discussed Chorover and Schiller's (1966) motor disinhibition criticism of the PAR/ECS aspect of this work (cf. p. 5 above). Several arguments against this criticism should be noted at this time. First, even if Chorover and Schiller's explanation is correct for the PAR situation employed by Bureš, it does not explain the results on discrimination reversal, where it is not readily apparent how motor disinhibition would be involved. Second, Bureš and Burešová's results with CSD on the PAR were qualitatively similar to their results with ECS. Although it does not seem unreasonable that ECS with its resulting firing of millions of neurons might cause hyperexcitation and thence motor facilitation, one would expect CSD, which has a depressant effect, to do the opposite. Behaviorally then, by Chorover and Schiller's view, ECS should lead to impairment of the PAR whereas CSD should not. The data of Bureš and Buresová provide quite the opposite result. In a recent paper Schneider (1967) reviews the more recent work on CSD and memory and arrives at the curious conclusion that CSD does not prevent memory storage, but rather displaces it to non-depressed subcortical areas. The data indicate that when CSD interferes with memory (i.e., when it is given shortly after learning), the impairment is permanent, with no spontaneous improvement. If Schneider is correct, one must assume that displacement to subcortical structures is tantamount to prevention of storage since in neither case is there recovery. Given these data there seems to be little basis for Schneider's conclusion.

Despite discrepancies about such matters as the length of time during which treatment is effective in disrupting memory, the work on the effects on memory of interference with electrical activity can be placed within a coherent framework. First of all it is apparent that there is a period immediately subsequent to learning when memory is liable to attack, although the exact length of this period has been variously estimated from 10 sec. to 24 hr. Second it is clear that after this period has elapsed interference with brain electrical activity has no effect on memory. Thus, while the older theories of memory, which emphasize ongoing neural/electrical activity, may still explain recent or short-term memory, long-term memory is dependent upon some other process.

In the next chapters, after discussing the theoretical and biochemical requirements for a memory molecule, we shall review the evidence supporting the role of specific chemical substances in memory and learning.

chapter

II

THE NATURE
OF THE
MEMORY MOLECULE

Behavioral events, as we have noted, must ultimately be the result of nervous system activity. Thus, even though we may conclude that most of memory is not dependent upon *ongoing* neural activity, it must somehow affect neural activity if learning is to be translated into performance. Since synaptic transmission comprises a most important aspect of nervous function this seems a likely site for the interface between memory and performance. The fact that transmission at the synapse is chemical in nature is one major reason for the belief that memory, if it is not based on ongoing neural activity, may be chemical in nature. Another factor contributing to this view is the rise to prominence in the last 15 years of the field of molecular biology. With the elucidation of the genetic code as a chemical "message" on the DNA helix, it was a short step to the idea that if genetic information is stored and utilized chemically, perhaps other, *e.g.*, learned, information is stored in a similar manner. It is this sort of evidence which has led, in the last decade and a half, to the view that memory, or at least established memory, is probably the result of some chemical alteration.

Molar Approaches

Given the premise that memory is somehow encoded and stored by chemical means, one comes to the problem of the nature of this chemical code. There are two ways to approach this problem. The first, termed by Gaito and Zavala (1964) the molar approach, looks at the synapse itself to find the changes involved in memory and stems from the fact that behavior is the result of synaptic activity. It is this approach which has led to the work of Krech's group, which has primarily investigated acetylcholine (ACh) and acetylcholinesterase levels (these chemicals being critical in synaptic transmission) in the brain as a function of the experience of the organism. The work of this group has not attacked the problem of the chemical basis of memory directly, but has shown that experiential factors can profoundly affect the structural and biochemical development of the brain.

Another form of the molar approach is that of Overton (1959) who holds that learning is facilitated by a decrease in calcium ion concentration at the synapse and retarded by an increase. Overton's view is that there is set up in learning a reverberating circuit which must last 30 seconds in order for memory to "set," this latter process being the result of displacement of calcium ion from the synapse by the acetic acid product of ACh hydrolysis, thereby making it difficult for further change to take place in that synapse.

Although there is some (largely indirect) evidence to support the molar views, Gaito and Zavala (1964) point out two major difficulties in this approach. First, both the Krech and the Overton theories are based on the view that the gross assay measures they employ are actually reflecting the concentrations of chemicals operating at the synapse. The validity of this assumption is open to question in view of the lack of refinement of present methodology. Second, the molar views deal strictly with excitatory phenomena, and further, with only one supposed neural transmitter, namely acetylcholine. The wisdom of this exclusive concern with ACh is dubious in light of the present view that there may be not one but many neural transmitters (cf. McLennan, 1963). The preoccupation with excitatory processes is not a new one—much of the early neurological work on learning (e.g. Hebb, 1949) dealt only with excitation and viewed inhibition as a lack of facilitation. The more modern view of the nervous system has come to recognize inhibition as an important process (as did Pavlov). Certain chemicals, notably gamma-amino butyric acid, have been identified as possibly serving the role of inhibitory transmitters (McLennan, 1963). Additionally, certain parts of the nervous system, e.g., Renshaw cells, are now recognized as inhibitory centers (Ochs, 1966). Indeed, one school of thought holds that the nervous system operates *exclusively* by inhibitory processes with facilitation operating as a double negative process of inhibition of inhibitors (cf. Ruch, Patton, Woodbury and Towe, 1965). In view of this, the exclusive concern of the molar approach with excitatory process is questionable.

Molecular Approaches

A second approach is that which Gaito and Zavala (1964) characterize as the molecular view. Katz and Halstead, in 1950, suggested that neurons contain protein molecules in random configurations which become ordered by impulses coming into the neuron. More recently interest has focused upon the nucleic acids, and still more recently, it has shifted back to proteins. After establishing criteria for the evaluation of the various candidates for the role of memory molecule we shall review in the ensuing chapters the evidence on some of the foremost contenders. Various investigators (*e.g.*, Gaito, 1963; Dingman and Sporn, 1964) have set up lists of criteria for the memory molecule. The following is in part a synthesis of these lists, along with key words for each criterion:

1. *Lability*—the molecule must be able to be affected by extra-organismic agents, so that information in the form of input to the CNS can be processed and stored.
2. *Stability* or replicability—the molecule, once changed, must either be stable in order to permanently store the information, or it must be able to be replicated exactly, which would have the same end result.
3. *Size*—the molecule must be of sufficient size and complexity to encode complicated information within itself.

Besides these specific criteria, there are more obvious ones, *e.g.* presence in the central nervous system, known role in neural metabolism, etc.

In addition to these criteria known facts about memory strongly suggest some heterogeneous macromolecular substrate. While less complex molecules than the nucleic acids and proteins might conceivably fulfill the three criteria—even that of size—it is difficult to conceive of how a molecule such as C_8H_{18} (octane) could encode information—any rearrangement of the carbon or hydrogen atoms leads to a substance identical to the original. In order to form meaningful rearrangements, it is necessary to add other parts, *e.g.*, amine groups, phosphate groups, hydroxyl ions, etc., to the system, and it is desirable, as well, to work with larger functional units than single atoms, ions, or radicals.

It is in the complex sequences of bases, nucleosides, and amino acids (see Chapter III) of the nucleic acid and protein molecules that there is adequate storage space for information. Crick (1954) has stated that if information is stored in the DNA molecule in "words" composed of 3-base sequences, the possible combinations of "words" is in the millions. Further, nucleic acids and proteins are highly replicable, and, with the possible exception of DNA, are quite liable to change by environmental influences. The attractiveness of nucleic acids and proteins as possible memory molecules has led to three separate but related lines of research in the last few years, investigating memory functions of RNA, DNA, and proteins.

A word of caution must be injected at this point. For a number of reasons, to be noted below, it is both convenient and appropriate for this review to concentrate on single substances as potential memory molecules. The possibility must be noted, however, that the memory substrate might consist not of a single molecule, but of a molecular complex or system consisting of several nucleic acids and/or proteins acting together. By far the greatest amount of research and theorizing to this time has, however, been concerned with single molecule models, and so we shall concentrate our discussion on these. It is, however, well to note that as researchers in this area are becoming more sophisticated, so too are their models.

chapter
III

BASIC
CHEMICAL
CONSIDERATIONS

Proteins and nucleic acids, because of the extremely large size of their molecules, are termed macromolecular substances. Both of these types of chemicals are essential to life and normal metabolism. At this time we shall briefly review some of the basic facts about their structure and function.

Proteins

Proteins comprise a wide variety of the most complex chemical substances in the body. All have in common large amounts of nitrogen and the presence of simpler compounds called amino acids of which the proteins are made up. Amino acids, of which there have been some 20 to 30 isolated to date, take the chemical form $RCH(NH_2)COOH$ where R may be any organic radical (or, as in the case of glycine, the simplest amino acid, R may be hydrogen).

Amino acids combine by means of peptide bonds in which the alpha amino group of one amino acid attaches to the alpha carboxyl group of another (with the elimination of a water molecule) to form an amide linkage. The resulting compound is a protein intermediate called a peptide; these conjugate to form polypeptide chains and proteins (White, Handler, and Smith, 1959). The nature and chemical activity of a protein are determined not only by the identity of its constituent amino acids and by their relative quantities, but also by the sequence into which these are arranged.

Proteins are generally classified into five classes on the basis of their solubility. More important for our purposes is the distinction which is generally made between "simple" proteins, *i.e.*, those which decompose completely into their constituent amino acids, and "conjugated" proteins which are formed by the interaction of proteins with nonprotein organic compounds. These yield on decomposition compounds known as "prosthetic groups." The nucleoproteins implicated in chemical theories of learning and memory are of the conjugated types, and the nucleic acids are prosthetic groups (White *et al.*, 1959).

Further mention should be made of enzymes, an important class of proteins which function in cell systems as catalysts. They have been characterized by Fruton and Simmonds (1958) as the machinery whereby cellular raw materials are converted into the complex products needed for metabolism Enzymes are, in general, highly specific in their catalytic function. The enzyme ribonuclease (RNase), for example, has as its sole function the cleavage of RNA at the phosphate linkage (see below). Another important class of enzymes is the proteases, the function of which is cleavage of protein molecules into their constituent groups.

Nucleic Acids

Nucleic acids are made up of three basic units: sugars, bases, and phosphate molecules.

Sugars

The nucleic acids contain as their sugar components pentoses, or five-carbon sugars. Deoxyribonucleic acid (DNA) and ribonucleic acid (RNA) differ, as the names imply, in the form of the sugar molecule. Figure 1a shows the structure of

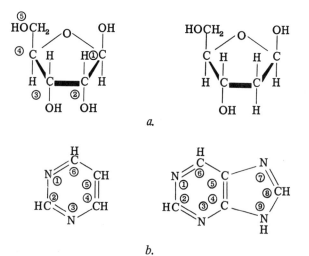

Fig. 1a: *Structures of ribose (left) and deoxyribose (right).*
b: *Prototype forms of pyrimidine (left) and purine (right).*

ribose and deoxyribose, and it can be seen that the only difference occurs at the number 2 carbon. In ribose there is a hydroxyl group, whereas in deoxyribose this is replaced by a hydrogen atom (White *et al.*, 1959).

Bases

Bases are divided according to their molecular structure into purines and pyrimidines. Figure 1b shows the basic or prototype form of these bases. DNA and RNA each contain two purine bases and two pyrimidine bases. Both DNA and RNA contain cytosine which is a pyrimidine, adenine and guanine, both of which are purines. A difference between the nucleic acids is that DNA contains the pyrimidine base thymine while RNA contains uracil. The structures of these five bases are shown in Figure 2.

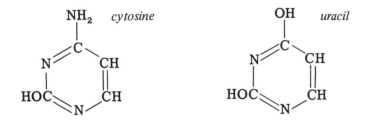

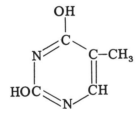

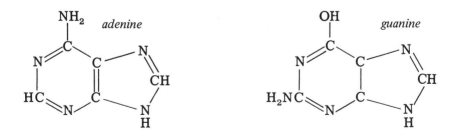

Fig. 2: *Structures of bases in RNA and DNA.*

Nucleosides

The combination of a base and a sugar molecule forms a complex known as a nucleoside. The ribose nucleosides are named for the parent base, with the suffix *-osine* added for purines, and *-idine* for pyrimidines. The naming of the nucleosides is given in Table 1.

TABLE 1
Naming of Nucleosides and Nucleotides

Bases	Nucleosides	Nucleotides
Adenine	Adenosine	Adenylic acid
Guanine	Guanosine	Guanylic acid
Cytosine	Cytidine	Cytidylic acid
Thymine	Thymidine	Thymidylic acid
Uracil	Uridine	Uridylic acid

Nucleotides

Nucleotides are formed by the addition of a phosphoric acid molecule (H_3PO_4) to C_3 or C_5 of the nucleoside sugar. The nucleotides are named either specifically (*e.g.*, adenosine 5'-phosphate, 3'-phosphate, 2'-phosphate), or non-specifically (*e.g.*, adenosine monophosphate, AMP). In nucleic acid work, however, it is more common to name them as acids (see Table 1). Figure 3 shows the structures of the five nucleotides of importance in discussing RNA and DNA.

The Structure and Biosynthesis of RNA

In RNA, the number of adenine—and cytosine-based nucleotides is equal to that of guanine—and uracil-based nucleotides. Furthermore, the total number of purine nucleotides is equal to that of pyrimidine nucleotides, and the molar ratios of adenine to uracil (A/U ratio) and guanine to cytosine (G/C ratio) are equal to one (Grossman, 1967).

The RNA molecule is formed by the joining of nucleotides into long chains, termed polynucleotides. The internucleotide lines are formed by the phosphoric acid molecules, which esterify to bridge between the 3' carbon of one sugar molecule and the 5' carbon of another (White *et al.*, 1959). Grossman (1967) points out that it follows from this that RNA molecules can differ only in the sequence of the bases in the polynucleotide chain, or in the length of the chain itself. Three ways of referring to nucleic acid structure have been distinguished: the *primary structure* consists of the bases making up the nucleic acid macromolecule. That is, the primary structure of RNA consists of the bases adenine, guanine, cytosine, and uracil, and is the same for all RNA molecules.

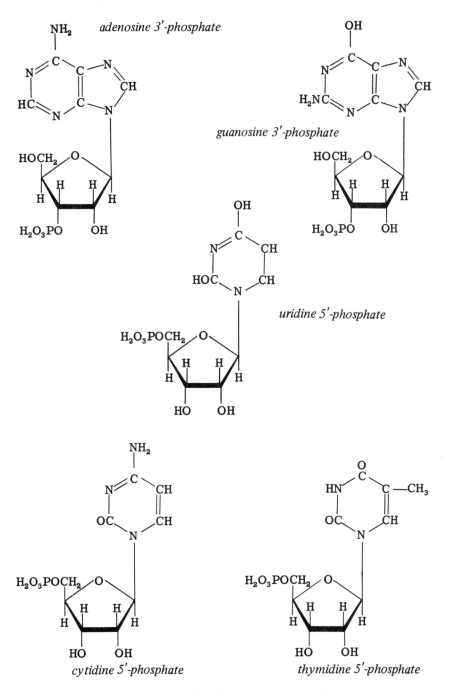

Fig. 3: *Structures of nucleotides in RNA and DNA.*

The *secondary structure* consists of all the sequences in which these bases are arranged, and so will differ from one molecule to another. The *tertiary structure* consists of the physical conformation of the entire molecule.

Three classes of intracellular RNA may be distinguished based on molecular weight and function. These are "soluble" or "transfer" RNA (sRNA) which is found in the cytoplasm, and has a molecular weight of 20 to 40 thousand; "messenger" RNA (mRNA) which is found in the nucleus, and has a molecular weight of 200 to 500 thousand; and ribosomal RNA (rRNA) which is found in the ribosomes, and has a molecular weight of about two million.

The biosynthesis of RNA occurs, at least in part, on the chromosome. Because it is presently held that all RNA synthesis is dependent upon DNA, it is assumed that all RNA is formed in the nucleus. Actually relatively little is known about RNA biosynthesis, especially that of sRNA and rRNA, and it is possible that there exists some DNA-independent synthesis of these forms. In the case of mRNA, at least, it seems clear that the molecule is formed by DNA which breaks to form a single-stranded template, allowing a "negative copy" to be made of RNA (RNA-DNA hybrid). The RNA strand then breaks off and exists independently. The existence of DNA-RNA hybrids has been demonstrated in cell systems such as the bacteria *Escherichia coli* (White *et al.,* 1959).

The Structure and Biosynthesis of DNA

At the most basic level the structure of DNA is very similar to that of RNA. The same structural constraints on the base ratios which were discussed above for RNA hold for DNA with the exception of the substitution of thymine and its nucleoside and nucleotide for uracil and its conjugates. Internucleotide links are formed in the same way for DNA as for RNA, and so various DNA molecules, like RNA, can differ only in their base sequences and their absolute length.

The major difference between the DNA and RNA molecules is that where RNA is complete as a single strand, DNA in mammalian cells is composed of two strands of the type shown in Figure 4a. The "spines" of the two strands are formed of deoxyribose molecules joined by the $3'\ 5'$ phosphodiester bridges described above for RNA, with the bases attached at angles to the main axis of the strand. The chains are joined together by hydrogen bonds between the bases, with the amino group of one base joined to the keto group of another. In each case, a purine and a pyrimidine base are paired. This gives rise to two chains which are not identical, but are complementary; for example, AGTCAAGTGGCC and TCAGTTCACCGG. The hydrogen-bonded double chain is shown in Figure 4b.

Because of the stearic requirements of hydrogen bonding, the double strand cannot remain linear, but is twisted into a right-hand helix. This structure, first elucidated by Watson and Crick in 1953 (*cf.* White *et al.*, 1959), is now accepted as the structure of DNA, and is shown in Figure 5.

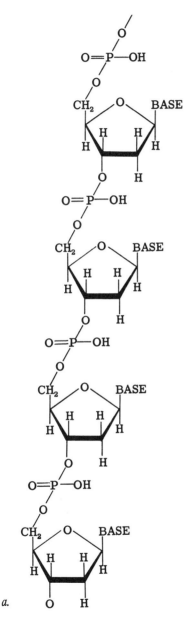

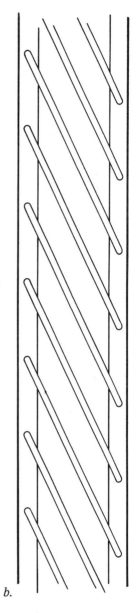

Fig. 4a: *Structure of a single strand of DNA.*
b: *Structure of the DNA double strand.*

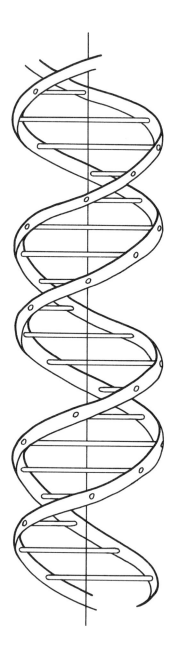

Fig. 5: *Structure of the DNA double helix*
(adapted from Grossman, 1967).

Biosynthesis of Protein

Both nucleic acids play a vital role in protein biosynthesis. *In vivo* formation of protein takes place in two stages—the formation of the peptide bonds to form small polypeptides, and the selection and arrangement of the polypeptides to determine the amino acid sequence of the resultant protein molecule.

Amino acids do not readily coalesce to form proteins but must be activated. This takes place in the cell by means of the energy compound ATP. White *et al.*, (1959, p. 599) summarize this activation as follows:

(1)   Amino acid + ATP + enzyme → amino acyl
AMP-enzyme + PP_i

(2)   Amino acyl-AMP-enzyme + sRNA → amino
acyl-sRNA + AMP + enzyme

Sum: Amino acid + ATP + sRNA → amino acyl-sRNA
+ AMP + PP_i

In this two-step reaction, a mixed carboxylic-phosphoric anhydride complexed with an enzyme (an amino acyl synthetase) is formed in the first step. It is thought at present that there is a specific form of sRNA for each amino acid; this sRNA joins onto the anhydride-enzyme complex at the amino acyl end, causing the AMP (adenosine monophosphate, the low-energy degradation product of ATP) and the enzyme to drop off. This reaction results in the formation of an amino acyl-sRNA complex, AMP, and inorganic phosphate. The sRNA then transfers the activated amino acid to the ribosomes where the amino acids are joined.

For this stage, which is the actual synthesis of the proteins, information for the arrangement of the amino acids comes from DNA in the nucleus of the cell. It is felt (Karlson, 1963) that the DNA of the chromosomes forms a negative copy of itself in mRNA, as described above. The function of the mRNA is to activate the ribosomes for protein synthesis, and to code the amino acid sequence. It is now held (Karlson, 1963) that mRNA codes each amino acid as a "word" of three "letters." That is, each bit of information on the mRNA strand consists of a sequence of three bases. This gives rise to a possibility of 4^3 or 64 different "words," for the 23 amino acids found in proteins, so it might appear that some words have no amino acid attached to them, or are redundant. It is conceivable, however, that each amino acid is represented by two different words, one for when it appears inside a sequence and another to indicate that it falls at an end of a sequence (Karlson, 1963). Once the activated amino acids are arranged on the ribosome, peptide links are formed and the protein breaks away from the ribosome.

Enzyme Induction

In closing this chapter, mention should be made of the phenomenon of enzyme induction. This term refers to the process whereby the rate of synthesis of certain enzymes is greatly increased when the substrate upon which that enzyme acts enters the cell. For example, yeast cells continually produce at a low rate the enzyme beta-galactoside, which cleaves the sugar lactose. However, when lactose is placed in the medium the rate of synthesis of beta-galactoside increases severalfold. Of particular interest to us here is the fact that certain compounds other than the substrate are also capable of inducing the production of enzymes identical with the naturally occurring (non-induced) enzyme. Since these induced enzymes are being produced *de novo* from amino acids, the inducer, whether natural substrate or not, is effectively causing protein synthesis. The mechanism for this phenomenon is unknown (Karlson, 1963).

Having discussed these biochemical processes, we may now proceed to a review of the evidence on DNA, RNA, and protein as potential memory molecules.

chapter
IV

DNA AS THE
MEMORY MOLECULE

Because of the major role recently proposed for DNA in the encoding and transmission of genetic information (Crick, 1954), it was natural for this compound to come under close scrutiny as a candidate for the encoding of experiential information.

At first glance DNA seems most promising in this respect. It is highly stable and of sufficient size to encode information. Furthermore, it already holds an information-encoding function, and because science assumes some parsimony in life systems, it might reasonably be expected to impress a dual function on the DNA molecule.

There is very little data on DNA metabolism during behavioral events. A number of European experimenters have, however, looked at nucleic acid changes as a result of various physiological manipulations. Vladimirov, Ivanov, and Pravdina (1954) showed that administration of narcotics and mechanical irritation of nerve cells resulted in a change in RNA metabolism (to be discussed below), but caused no change in DNA quantity or activity. In a similar study, Mihailović, Janković, Petković, and Isaković (1957), while noting a marked change in RNA content, found no effect at all of ECS on DNA metabolism. Brodsky (1957) replicated and extended the work of Vladimirov *et al.* on the effect of narcotics on DNA metabolism, obtaining similar results.

In an early study of cellular DNA concentrations, Vendrely and Vendrely (1949) compared amounts of DNA in the nuclei of the cells of various organs both within and between individuals and species. They remarked upon the extreme constancy of the amount of DNA, and concluded that if DNA constitutes the genetic material (this is now held to be the case), all mammals might possess approximately the same genetic apparatus. In a later paper (1956) the same authors reviewed the DNA constancy theory, and once again emphasized the extreme constancy of the amount of nuclear DNA across mammalian species. They further stated that it has been shown that DNA is extremely resistant to change by any normal outside influence. Yoshida (1958) confirmed this view by microspectrophotometric studies on DNA of the ox retina.

Kornberg (1960), in a review of the biosynthetic processes of DNA, stated unequivocally that there is no evidence that DNA, once formed, ever changes, or that the biosynthetic process can be influenced by the sort of electrochemical processes occurring in nerve cells. The genetic template molecules must be present in order for DNA to be formed. Furthermore, as Grossman (1967) pointed out, even if the DNA molecule were broken by the electrical impulse there is no way for the parts to rearrange to form a new molecule and thereby possibly encode the memory. He went on to state that

> the only way in which the base sequence of a DNA molecule can be altered . . . is through the action of a mutagenic agent; this substance produces basic chemical changes in the pyrimidine and purine bases so that compounds not normally present in DNA are substituted for one of the four bases (p. 873).

It is in this stability that the case *against* DNA as the memory molecule finds its strongest support. Because, as Kornberg (1960) pointed out, if there is no way to change DNA short of use of a mutagenic agent, it would be virtually impossible for behavioral experience to become encoded. Furthermore, because mutations are generally sterile or non-viable, such a function for DNA would be extremely maladaptive. At a more concrete level, no evidence for the existence of unusual bases in DNA has ever been presented, and so it seems reasonable to conclude that this cannot be the memory molecule (Grossman, 1967).

Gaito (1961; 1963) is the only theorist to have seriously held a theory of memory based upon changes in DNA base sequences in the light of the stability of the compound. He suggested that the DNA of nerve cells might be different in some important fashion from that of liver and pancreas cells (those generally studied by biochemists) in that it might be labile and not involved in genetic transmission. There is no experimental support for this view, and by 1964 Gaito had abandoned it to concentrate on the role of RNA in memory. This led Gaito to his recent development of a DNA-activation theory which is still in its formative stages and is too complex for the present discussion. (For a detailed review see Gaito, 1966b.)

It seems reasonably safe to conclude, therefore, that DNA may be ruled out as a possible memory molecule, except, as we shall discuss below, in a very peripheral, subsidiary role.

chapter
V

RNA AS THE
MEMORY MOLECULE

Evidence on RNA as the memory molecule comes from several lines of research. Three of these will be reviewed in this chapter: work on RNA metabolism during behavioral events, work with drugs affecting RNA, and work with yeast RNA. Some of the major theories of RNA and memory will also be reviewed. The fourth line of evidence which comes from studies of inter-animal transfer of learning will be reviewed separately in Chapter VII.

RNA Metabolism During Behavioral Events

The term "behavioral events," which is used here after Pevzner (1966), is a general one encompassing a number of different sorts of manipulations. In this section we shall examine changes in RNA levels as a function of neural excitation, neural inhibition, and learning, both at the cellular and the organismic levels. The first two of these areas are reviewed extensively by Pevzner (1966), and so only a few studies will be cited in these areas as illustrations and the studies reviewed by Pevzner will be summarized.

Excitation

Pevzner reviewed thirteen experiments in which neural activity was moderately increased from base levels either by natural or artificial stimulation. Hydén (1943), for example, electrically stimulated cells of the spinal ganglia and found that with brief or intermittent stimulation the concentration of cytoplasmic RNA rapidly increased. In a later study (Hamberger and Hydén, 1945), it was found that with auditory stimulation (600 cps at 80 db) cytoplasmic RNA in the spiral ganglion of the cochlea increased by 80% to 100%. A similar effect was found in the vestibular ganglion by Hamberger and Hydén (1949), where RNA increased 30% to 100% after oscillation of the animal for six minutes. Vladimirov *et al.* (1954) stimulated skin receptors electrically and obtained a 22% increase in RNA specific activity. Chitre, Chopra, and Talwar (1964) measured RNA specific activity in whole brain homogenates following a convulsive dose of the drug Metrazol (pentylenetetrazol) and found a 27% increase during the preconvulsive (excitatory) stage. In a review of 13 studies by Pevzner (1966) an average increase of 70.92% to 88.61% was obtained as a result of various types of neural excitation. Most importantly, in none of the 13 cases was there a decrease or even a case of no change after excitation.

Inhibition

Studies of neural inhibition have taken many forms, ranging from induced exhaustion to drug poisoning. Hamberger and Hydén (1945) studied the effects of acoustic trauma upon RNA content of spiral ganglion cells. They found that a revolver shot one foot from the animal's head caused a 30% to 60% decrease in cytoplasmic RNA. Russian investigators (cited by Pevzner, 1966) found that narcosis induced by amobarbital sodium or by alcohol also caused decreases of 30% to 40% in cortex and in spinal motor neurons. Gomirato and Baggio (*cf.* Pevzner, 1966) measured total cellular RNA in spinal motor neurons and found a 35% decrease after their animals were worked to exhaustion. Falbe-Hansen and Pakkenberg (1963) found that poisoning of the hair cells of the inner ear by arsacetin led to a 22% to 28% decrease in cytoplasmic RNA content in the spiral and vestibular ganglia. Pevzner reviewed 20 studies of this type, with an average decrease of 18.85% to 28.05%. It is interesting to note that in this case, there are two studies which show an increase in RNA. Both of these used barbiturate narcosis, and found increases of 18% and 20%. The reason for these increases is unclear, and they would seem to be outweighed by the contrasting evidence which has been cited.

Learning

Relatively little work has been done measuring RNA changes as a function of learning, since this sort of study requires extremely sophisticated biochemical analyses. It is to be expected that in any learning situation cells of the receptors and cortical areas involved would increase in their RNA content simply as a function of excitation as reviewed above. Therefore, it is usually necessary to look for qualitative rather than quantitative RNA changes.

The first strong, although still indirect, evidence for RNA changes as a function of learning came from the work of Morrell (1961), who developed what he termed an analog model for cellular learning. This model consists of a pathological process using the same neural pathways available to normal processes, in which "changes in synaptic organization, cellular excitability, and cellular chemistry have been demonstrated on a time scale comparable to behavioral learning" (p. 375).

Morrell's procedure consists of local application of an ethyl chloride spray to a 2 mm area of cortex. This leads within a few hours to the development of seizure-type electrical activity at the periphery of the area, and within a few days to the development of a secondary focus of seizure activity in the homologous area of the opposite hemisphere. This Morrell terms the "mirror focus." After a species-specific length of time has passed the secondary focus becomes independent of the primary, and ablation of the primary focus does not affect the activity of the secondary focus. Morrell suggests, both on the basis of these data and of direct cortical recordings, that the mirror focus area may be

a ganglionic network in which spontaneous and evoked activity have been chronically altered as a result of experimental alteration of its environmental input in the form of continuous epileptiform bombardment (p. 379).

The establishment of the mirror focus may be prevented by section of the corpus callosum either before establishment of the primary focus, or within 24 hours afterward. Alternatively, the callosum may be left intact, and the mirror focus area partially isolated by subpial aspiration within the same time period. This latter procedure deprives the area of all subcortical connections, as well as most of its transcortical links to its own hemisphere. The callosal pathway remains intact, and is the only source of input to the area. Morrell interpreted these data to mean that the establishment of the independent mirror focus requires at least two forms of input.

Morrell then considered the problem of whether the change in excitability is due to the setting up of reverberatory circuits, or rather to structural changes in the cells of the network—that is, whether it is electrical or chemical in nature. After surgical isolation of the primary focus, seizure activity there was abolished while that of the mirror focus was unaffected. The mirror focus was then similarly isolated, leaving it likewise inactive. Chronic recording electrodes were then affixed to the surface of the cortex in the focus areas, and the animal was returned to its cage for several months, during which time no return of seizure discharge was observed. After several months had elapsed, an acute preparation was made of the animal, with gross electrodes placed on the surface of the now-isolated mirror focus, and one to four microelectrodes inserted into the slab at depths of 500 to 1000 micra. The convulsant drug Metrazol was then placed upon the adjacent normal cortex. This caused seizure activity in this area, which slowly spread across the gap into the isolated area. Morrell concluded

the ease with which such . . . transmission can be demonstrated in isolated epileptic cortex makes it clear that the increased ... irritability has persisted in the cellular elements of the mirror region despite the fact that the spontaneous manifestation of this irritability was abolished by the neuronal isolation ... the mirror focus is a region which has not only "learned" to behave in terms of paroxysmal discharge, but which "remembers" this behaviour even after months of inactivity. The isolation experiment has excluded reverberating impulses as the basis of the changed electrical behavior and makes it necessary to search for structural alterations (pp. 383-84).

Given the assumption that there is a structural or chemical change, and that this may be localized in the cells of the mirror focus, Morrell reasoned that since changes in ion distribution are too transient to provide the memory system and brain protein turnover is too high, "the search for an organizer substance leads one logically to the nucleic acids and, for events which are primarily cytoplasmic, to the ribonucleic acids" (pp. 385-386). RNA staining by the methyl green pyronin method was done in sections through the mirror focus area. For control purposes every third section was treated with RNAse prior to staining, to show that RNA was indeed the substance being stained. The sections were compared with sections from other, non-involved, brain areas, similarly stained. It was found that the stain concentrated highly in the mirror focus region, indicating large concentrations of RNA in this area.

In view of the evidence reviewed in the preceding sections, it is not surprising that the excitatory activity going on in the mirror focus area causes an increase in RNA content of the cells in the area. Morrell noted this, stating that it is more of interest here to consider "... the relationship of RNA to the coding of information necessary to effectuate permanent alteration of cellular excitability" (p. 389). He proceeded to state the hypothesis that cells in the mirror focus are altered by changes in distribution of RNA, perhaps linked with protein or phospholipids, and since the "learning" and "memory" shown in the mirror focus are considered analogous to the corresponding behavioral phenomena, this may represent the chemical basis of memory.

It should be noted that these last points, *i.e.*, the interpretation of the RNA staining results as evidence for qualitative as well as quantitative changes in RNA, represent assumptions on Morrell's part and that these assumptions have no basis in the data. RNA staining, as Chow pointed out in the discussion following Morrell's paper, is extremely difficult to interpret even with relation to *quantitative* changes and tells nothing about *qualitative* changes at all. From a *post hoc* standpoint, in the light of Hydén's results (v. infra) it seems possible that Morrell is justified in these assumptions but there is no firm evidence that he is.

Morrell's experiments may be considered to be a study of learning on the cellular or molecular level (*cf.* p. 27). Beginning in 1962, Hydén (Hydén and Egyházi, 1962a, 1963, 1964; Hydén and Lange, 1965) studied the effects of learning tasks of a more usual sort upon neural RNA.

In the first of this series of studies (Hydén and Egyházi, 1962a) three groups of rats were used. In one group, rats were trained to walk up a tight-wire placed at an angle of 45 degrees to the floor of their cage in order to obtain food. A second group, designated functional controls, were rotated slowly in a centrifuge to control for the vestibular stimulation involved in learning the balancing task. A third group, designated controls, were not trained but were kept on a low-calorie dietary regimen. As would be expected, absolute amounts of RNA in Deiters' (vestibular) nucleus cells increased both in experimental and functional control animals. In addition, however, significant changes occurred in the amounts of the various bases contained in the nuclear RNA. Amounts of adenine increased and of uracil decreased (A/U ratio = 1.06 in controls vs. 1.35 in experimentals), and the purine-to-pyrimidine (A+G/C+U) ratio likewise increased (0.91 vs. 1.03). Hydén and Egyházi comment upon the failure to detect transfer of the changed RNA from the nucleus to the cytoplasm, interpreting this as possible evidence for transfer of only minute amounts, as in the transfer of mRNA in protein synthesis. The nuclear RNA changes were taken to be indicative of activation of the chromosomes to produce mRNA with highly specific base ratios in line with Hydén's early theory (see below).

In the second experiment in this series (Hydén and Egyházi, 1963) glial RNA changes were measured as a function of learning the same task. Since the glia have been shown to act as a functional unit with the neuron (Hydén and Pigon, 1960; Hydén, 1962), with linked systems for RNA biosynthesis (Egyházi and Hydén, 1961; Hydén and Egyházi, 1962b), changes in glial RNA would be expected to follow a course similar to that of neuronal RNA. This was found to be the case although changes in the glia were not identical to those of the neurons. In this study, as in the prior study, measurements were of Deiter's nucleus cells. The increased amounts of RNA observed in the 1962 study were not found in this study, however; also it was noted that base ratio changes disappeared after 24 hours.

These two studies appear to provide *indirect* evidence supporting the theory that memory is encoded as changes in RNA base sequences, but no direct relation of base changes to learning has been established. Although the method used has some face validity there are certain difficulties. First of all, there is the question of whether any learning is actually going on. The rats "learned" to walk the wire very quickly (1-2 trials), and there is some doubt whether such an agile animal as the rat has anything to learn in this situation. The authors state (1962) that some Ss performed perfectly from the first trial. While "no-trial learning" is not *prima facie* evidence of absence of learning, it does seem to indicate that the response was in the animal's repertoire prior to the inception of the experiment, and required little if any reinforcement to bring it out. The fact that the changed RNA did not appear to transfer from the nucleus to the cytoplasm may indicate, as noted above, transfer of minute amounts, but it may also indicate that the system was not stimulated enough to *cause* transfer of significant amounts. Second, the use of Deiter's nucleus as the site of measurement of the changes is open to question. While it is not unreasonable to expect that some changes might take place in a primary sensory relay station early in learning, it does not seem reasonable to look for long-term or lasting changes there. These long-term changes seem to occur in the cortex and to be more and more "cerebrized" as learning proceeds (Flexner, 1966).

In a third experiment (Hydén and Egyházi, 1964), a method was employed which avoided these objections. Rats were trained to obtain food from a tube in a manner that required the use of one paw to grasp the food. After learning this they were forced to use only their non-dominant paw to obtain the food, thus forcing a transfer of handedness. The motor cortices of the dominant and non-dominant hemispheres were then compared for amount of RNA and base composition of RNA in the paw area. As in the earlier experiments, increased purine-to-pyrimidine ratios were observed. In addition to the increased A+G/C+U ratio, a decreased G+C/A+U ratio was found, suggesting the formation of RNA similar to mRNA. One cautionary note must be injected at this point: it is possible that changes in base ratios such as we have been discussing might constitute nothing more than a statistical artifact resulting from the analysis of a pool of several RNA species in quantities which varied between analyses.

In 1965, Hydén and Lange replicated both the handedness and the balancing experiments, obtaining similar chemical changes. This, along with the results of Hydén and Egyházi (1964), indicates that the increased purine-to-pyrimidine ratios as a result of learning may be a real effect, and that changes in RNA base ratios may have a role in the encoding of memory.

Research with Drugs Affecting RNA

If RNA is the memory substrate, then it should be possible to facilitate or inhibit memory by means of drugs which, respectively, enhance or interfere with RNA synthesis. Research in this area has been mainly with three drugs: 8-azaguanine and actinomycin-D to interfere with RNA synthesis, and magnesium pemoline to enhance it. The malononitrile dimer 1,1,3-tricyano-2-amino-propene (TCAP) has also been used as an RNA enhancing agent, but since the main effect of this drug appears to be upon protein synthesis, it will be discussed in the next chapter.

8-azaguanine

The drug 8-azaguanine, as the name implies, is a derivative of the purine base guanine. It functions as an antimetabolite of RNA, in that the RNA molecule, after alteration by incorporation of 8-azaguanine, no longer functions as normal RNA but instead is relatively inert metabolically. Dingman and Sporn (1961) showed by radioactive tracing that 8-azaguanine-2-C^{14} (radioactively labeled 8-azaguanine) injected intracisternally is incorporated into brain RNA. They tested rats for performance, learning, and recall on a water maze task following injection of 136 μg of 8-azaguanine in a bicarbonate solution, and found no difference between drug and placebo groups in their ability to perform the sensory and motor tasks required to swim the maze. Furthermore, there was no difference in recall of a previously learned maze path. A difference between groups did occur, however, when a learning measure was employed. In this experiment, rats were given 15 trials in the maze (intertrial interval of three minutes), with speed and error scores recorded. Although speed scores did not differ, as would be expected on the basis of the performance data in the first experiment, drug animals made on the average twice as many errors as did placebo animals, with the greatest difference appearing in the first five trials. From these results it appears that disruption of RNA metabolism affects learning, but does not affect the performance of already learned behavior. This leads to two possible conclusions. The first is that memory once encoded in RNA renders the RNA metabolically inert; this seems unlikely, however, since the readout function inherent in memory would seem to require at least some modicum of metabolic activity. The second is that it is possible that RNA subserves memory in the encoding process while the storage function utilizes some other substrate. The data on protein as the memory molecule, to be reviewed in the next chapter, indicates that some other substrate having this function may indeed exist.

Chamberlain, Rothschild, and Gerard (1963) studied the effects of 8-azaguanine on a very different sort of situation. Like Morrell (see above, pp. 26-28) these investigators drew an analogy between behavioral learning and a pathological phenomenon. If a rat is subjected to a unilateral cerebellar lesion, then a postural asymmetry in the hind limbs results. This postural asymmetry can be abolished by a mid-thoracic spinal cord transection if this is performed immediately, but if sufficient time is allowed to elapse the asymmetry will persist despite transection of the cord. Since the asymmetry is considered to be the result of asymmetrical facilitatory stimulation via the descending spinal tracts, the motor nerves of the affected area seem to be undergoing a change of a nature analogous to learning, in that the postural asymmetry loses its dependence upon the presence or absence of this descending influence. Chamberlain et al. investigated the effects of 8-azaguanine (and of TCAP, to be discussed below) upon this phenomenon, which they referred to as spinal cord fixation time. In addition, they tested for effects of the drugs on avoidance learning and maze learning.

In the spinal cord fixation experiment, it was found that the average fixation time for injected and non-injected controls was 45 minutes. Intraperitoneal injection of 8-azaguanine increased this to 70 minutes. If the fixation phenomenon is considered analogous to a learning process, as Chamberlain et al. consider it, then injection of the nucleic acid antimetabolite, as in the Dingman and Sporn experiment, appears to have retarded "learning." In a maze-learning experiment animals were given nine of the twelve problems in the Hebb-Williams (1946) series. No difference was found as a result of the drug in either error or speed scores. In the bar-press avoidance task, animals injected with 8-azaguanine did not differ from controls in latency of response or on mean number of avoidance responses over three days of testing.

As Chamberlain *et al.* pointed out, their data for the Hebb-Williams maze are not really comparable to Dingman and Sporn's data for the water maze, because there are wide areas of divergence between the two studies. The most obvious of these is the use of the more effortful water maze in the Dingman and Sporn study, as opposed to the dry Hebb-Williams maze. A more important difference, however, is in the route of administration of the drug. Dingman and Sporn gave 136 μg of the drug intracisternally, while Chamberlain *et al.* gave 50, 150, or 200 mg/kg of body weight intraperitoneally to rats weighing 350 to 400 gm. This results in average doses of 19, 56, and 75 mg respectively. While Dingman and Sporn were able to demonstrate that most or all of the material they injected intracisternally was absorbed into the brain, there is no evidence as to how much, if any, of the material gets through the blood-brain barrier following intraperitoneal administration.

The failure to pass the blood-brain barrier might account for the results obtained by Chamberlain *et al.* It would not seem necessary for the drug to enter the brain in order to act on the motor neurons of the spinal cord to prolong fixation time. A more central action, however, would seem to be required for an effect upon the more complex inter-modality, sensory-motor problems of avoidance and maze learning. There is also the possibility, of course, that the metabolic processes involved in spinal cord fixation are not analogous to those involved in learning.

The case for an effect of 8-azaguanine on learning via RNA is, therefore, unclear. The results of Dingman and Sporn seem to indicate strongly that some effect does exist. The data of Chamberlain *et al.* are neither supportive of Dingman and Sporn nor contradictory, but are simply not comparable.

Actinomycin-D

The antibiotic actinomycin is believed to inhibit RNA synthesis by competitive interaction for the template site of DNA (Goldberg, Rabinowitz and Reich, 1962; 1963; Hurwitz, Furth, Malamy and Alexander, 1962). It affects only RNA *synthesis* and does not affect protein synthesis or RNA already synthesized and functioning (Reich, Franklin, Shotkin and Tatum, 1962).

Barondes and Jarvik (1964) were the first to investigate the effects of the intracerebral inoculation of actinomycin on memory in mice. By the use of radioactive tracer techniques it was found that this method of administration led to an 83% overall average inhibition of RNA synthesis. Because it was not possible to obtain total inhibition, the authors postulated that an alternate pathway might exist which is not liable to attack by actinomycin.

The behavioral task employed by Barondes and Jarvik was of the passive avoidance (see Chapter I) type, in which animals had to learn to inhibit walking in the apparatus. Despite the actinomycin-induced inhibition of RNA synthesis the drug animals learned and retained the response as well as controls. These results might be considered damaging to the view that RNA is involved in learning, were it not for the fact that doses of actinomycin of this magnitude almost invariably led to illness and death of the animals in a few hours. Specifically, all animals became diarrheic within 6 to 8 hours and died within 24 hours. Onset of toxic effects was preceded by decreased activity. Since the animals were tested four hours post-injection it does not seem unreasonable to assume that their performance on the passive avoidance task may have been "facilitated" by the toxic symptoms, because they may have been too sick to move.

In a later experiment (Cohen and Barondes, 1966a) a multiple injection technique was used which resulted in greater inhibition (94%-96%) of RNA synthesis. The animals still became ill, but this appeared to have been somewhat less severe than in the first experiment. Furthermore, the behavioral tasks employed were a Y-maze and a two-choice T-maze which the animals had to traverse in order to avoid shock. With the more active response the toxic effects of the drug would lead to a poorer rather than better performance.

Animals were run in the Y-maze 4 to 4.5 hours after injection. Drug-injected animals did not differ from injected or non-injected controls on acquisition or on retention after 1 and 4 hours. The two-choice T-maze was then used to test the animals on a more complex task and, again, no differences were found on either acquisition or retention. The authors concluded tentatively that "RNA synthesis is not required for memory storage in the intervals after learning which were studied" (p. 209). To investigate the possibility that RNA synthesis might become involved in memory storage at a later time, the few animals which survived were again tested in the double T-maze on the next day. They exhibited a high degree of savings. The authors feel that the implications of these results

argue against the encoding of memory in a specific RNA synthesized from a DNA template. Likewise, they argue against the participation of newly synthesized messenger-RNA in initial memory storage . . . the present experiments argue against the involvement of RNA synthesis in learning or in memory storage within 4 hr. of learning. The fact that animals could perform as well as they did under these conditions also indicates that the brain is not dependent on new RNA synthesis over a number of hours and can maintain its delicate intracellular and intercellular regulation without new RNA . . . a specific role for RNA synthesis in brain function remains to be demonstrated (pp. 210-211).[1]

Batkin, Woodward, Cole, and Hall (1966) tested carp on a T-maze visual discrimination task after administration of actinomycin either intracranially or intraperitoneally. They found that intracranially drug-treated fish made significantly *more* correct responses than controls over a 24 hour test. This result

[1] Copyright © 1966, Pergamon Press. Reprinted by permission of Pergamon Press.

is, of course, contrary both to the expectation that interference with RNA synthesis will be detrimental to learning and to the results of Cohen and Barondes indicating no effect of actinomycin on learning. Batkin *et al.* pointed out that blockage of template sites on the DNA molecule might create a pool of free RNA nucleotides, which might then be used in some memory encoding function. This view is supported by the fact that they obtain a similar enhancement with injections of yeast RNA (see below). While the notion of free nucleotides being involved in learning is an interesting one, it should be pointed out that the evidence to support it is entirely circumstantial. If this view were correct, we would expect a pool of free nucleotides in the brain, but there is no evidence for the existence of such a pool.

The most recent published report on antinomycin-D is that of Goldsmith (1967), who investigated the effect of intracerebral actinomycin on passive avoidance. The procedure is essentially that of Barondes and Jarvik (1964) with the important addition of RNA assays performed upon the same animals that were tested behaviorally. In one group, actinomycin administered intraventricularly was found to inhibit bar pressing in non-shocked animals. That is, the injection itself was sufficient to suppress bar pressing without the punishment used to establish the passive avoidance response.

The avoidance-trained groups were trained to press a bar for water. They were then surgically implanted with cannulae and retrained after a recovery period. After a stable response rate was again attained they were given two seconds of a two milliampere foot shock and removed from the apparatus. Two hours prior to testing they were injected with either actinomycin or saline solution. Upon replacement in the apparatus both saline- and drug-injected animals showed marked suppression of response. There was some indication that the shock was affecting the drug animals less than the saline animals, but none demonstrated amnesia for the shock.

The research with actinomycin-D seems to give considerable weight to the argument that DNA-dependent RNA synthesis is not involved in learning, although the failure to *completely* inhibit RNA synthesis leaves some room for doubt.

Magnesium Pemoline

In 1966, Glasky and Simon reported that the magnesium chelate of the central nervous stimulant *pemoline* (2-imino-5-phenyl-4-oxazolidinone-Abbott, 13397), manufactured by Abbott Laboratories as Cylert (pemoline with magnesium hydroxide-Abbott 30400), enhanced RNA polymerase activity *in vitro* and facilitated RNA production. At the same time Plotnikoff (1966a) administered magnesium pemoline, methamphetamine (a sympathomimetic stimulant), and methylphenidate (a non-sympathomimetic stimulant) to rats which were then taught a conditioned jump-out avoidance response. Animals given orally 5, 10, and 20 mg/kg of magnesium pemoline reached criterion more quickly and retained the response to a higher degree of proficiency than did the animals treated with the other stimulants. Plotnikoff characterized these doses of the drug as non-stimulant doses, since no increases in spontaneous activity were observed.

Bowman (1966) commented that while Plotnikoff's data do seem to indicate an acquisition effect, the retention effect may not be a real one since control rats had learned the response to a significantly poorer degree than the drug animals. Therefore, "the difference in retention may simply be a consequence of the difference in acquisition . . . and may therefore only reflect effects of the drug on acquisition processes" (p. 902).[2] In view of the evidence reviewed in Chapter I, one would expect to find an effect on the long-term process of retention rather than on the short-term process of acquisition if the drug is acting upon the chemical substrate of learning. Plotnikoff (1966b) stated in his reply to Bowman that it was difficult to train animals to the retention criterion in less than 50 trials, and, therefore, the fact that pemoline animals showed better retention was in itself proof of a retention effect. This, however, is not a valid argument because it does not answer Bowman's charge that the heightened retention was simply a result of a higher degree of learning.

In two subsequent papers, Plotnikoff (1966c; Plotnikoff and Meekma, 1967) extended his results showing enhancement of memory for an avoidance response. In the first he showed that magnesium pemoline attenuated the amnesic effects of ECS. While this may be so, it should be noted that this drug has some anticonvulsant effect, at least at high doses. Because the ECS-induced amnesia was not totally prevented it is possible to interpret Plotnikoff's data as the result of mild anticonvulsant effect. In the second study Plotnikoff and Meekma compared the effects of magnesium pemoline and pemoline alone on the enhancement of the jump-out avoidance response and found that magnesium pemoline was several times more potent. The objections of Bowman to Plotnikoff's original study apply as well to these two studies.

Since Plotnikoff's original publication (1966a), a number of studies have appeared which indicate that any effect of magnesium pemoline on learning is doubtful. Talland (1966), working with human subjects, found that the drug improved accuracy of performance on a task requiring sustained attention, a result found by Dureman with pemoline alone in 1962. Talland's data on a short-term memory task, along with those from the attention task, led him to conclude that magnesium pemoline has a non-specific alerting effect rather than a specific effect on memory function.

Cyert, Moyer, and Chapman (1967) attempted to extend Plotnikoff's jump-out results to a runway avoidance response. These investigators found no effect of oral administration of the drug on rate of learning or rate of extinction.

Smith (1967a, 1967b), in double-blind studies, failed to find evidence of facilitation by magnesium pemoline on a battery of human performance tests including verbal learning, motor learning, classical conditioning, visual and auditory short-term memory, arm-hand steadiness, and visual reaction time.

[2] Copyright 1967, American Association for the Advancement of Science.

These were administered as learning and retention tests, separated by 24 hours. The only significant difference he obtained was on the verbal learning test. The 25 mg dose group did not differ from controls but the 37.5 mg dose group performed significantly more poorly than either. Smith concluded that acute administration of the drug does not facilitate learning, memory, or performance.

Lubar, Boitano, Gurowitz, and Ain (1967) investigated the effects of chronic administration of magnesium pemoline on learning in the Hebb-Williams maze. Rats received daily intraperitoneal injections of 2.0 mg/100 gm body weight of magnesium pemoline daily for twelve days, during which they were trained on one problem per day of the Hebb-Williams series. Adaptation training on practice problems was given for twelve days prior to the start of the experiment to minimize emotionality and novelty effects. The drug was found to enhance performance, with drugged animals running faster and making fewer errors than controls. However, when an analysis of covariance was performed to adjust error scores for the effect of differential speeds, the difference between groups on number of errors was no longer significant. A three-way interaction (Drug x Problem x Trials) remained, however, indicating some residual effect on learning which was independent of the effect on performance. The authors concluded that the main effect of the drug appeared to be that of a stimulant.

In order to test the possibility that magnesium pemoline is mainly a stimulant (Talland, 1966; Lubar et al., 1967), and that Plotnikoff's data might simply reflect this effect, Gurowitz, Lubar, Ain and Gross (1967) investigated the effects of the drug on passive avoidance learning. The passive avoidance paradigm requires suppression of a response; therefore, as pointed out by Gurowitz and Lubar (1966), any agent which increases activity (such as a stimulant) should have a disruptive effect upon passive avoidance. In the Gurowitz et al. study, control animals took an average of 59.40 shocks over a 15 minute period, while drug animals took 102.65. The authors concluded:

> The data do not support the hypothesis that magnesium pemoline improves learning...our data lend additional support to the view that the effects of this drug are due to its action as a central stimulant . . . it seems reasonable to conclude that magnesium pemoline . . . [affects] performance but not learning (p. 20).

Thus, the data seem to indicate that magnesium pemoline—whatever its effect on RNA—does not affect learning. Further, very recent work questions its effect on RNA. Morris, Aghajanian, and Bloom (1967), with an in vivo technique, dispute the validity of Glasky and Simon's (1966) inference that because magnesium pemoline enhances RNA polymerase activity in vitro, it will do so in vivo. In fact Morris et al. fail to find any effect in vivo after intraperitoneal injection of the drug. This would seem to indicate that magnesium pemoline, although of possible use as a stimulant, has no value as a tool for the study of the biochemistry of learning.

Research Using Yeast RNA

It has been suggested that if RNA is the memory substrate, then it might be possible to facilitate learning and/or retention by increasing the available pool of RNA in the body. In attempts to do this, investigators over the past ten years have injected solutions of RNA extracted from yeast, a source relatively high in RNA yield. Two concurrent lines of research have developed, one using humans and the other animal subjects.

Research with Human Subjects

In 1958, Cameron reported an attempt to improve memory impairment in aged patients by the administration of a mixture of DNA and RNA in a physiological saline solution, given intravenously (4 g of DNA and 2 g of RNA daily), or orally (up to 75 g of RNA daily). All results on a battery of memory tests were termed "favorable," and 50% were termed "good." The best results were reported in patients with severe memory deficits and confusion.

In a later study (Cameron and Solyom, 1961), patients were given a larger battery of tests including the Wechsler memory scale, the counting test, and various conditioned response tests (for a complete list see Cameron, 1963). The patients, their families, and their associates were interviewed both prior to and after the institution of therapy. Two groups of patients were tested, one with mild memory deficits due to brain arteriosclerosis or senile dementia (29 and 8 subjects, respectively), and a second with more advanced deterioration due to brain damage or malnutrition (47 subjects). Subjects were administered either RNA or placebo pills, in a double-blind procedure. Both drug and placebo groups showed improvements in retention, along with general improvements in their condition, within three weeks. Speed of conditioning and retention of the conditioned response averaged twice its pre-therapy level. The only differences observed were not between groups as defined above but were between early and late onset of therapy, with those patients whose therapy began early in the course of the disorder showing the greater improvement.

In 1962, Cameron's group developed a technique whereby the RNA solution could be administered intravenously without the adverse side effects common with the earlier oral and intravenous administration (nausea, muscle cramps, and a fall in blood pressure—see Cameron, 1963). Furthermore, it allowed the administration of higher doses of RNA. In two studies using this method (Cameron, Solyom, Sved, and Wainrib, 1962; Cameron, Sved, Solyom, Wainrib, and Barik, 1963), these investigators were able to differentiate between the various disorders in terms of responsiveness to the therapy. In the three groups tested, it was found that the effects of RNA therapy were most marked in arteriosclerotic patients, were intermediate in presenile, and least successful in senile patients. In general, the finding of the 1958 study that therapy succeeded best in the severest cases has now been shown to be incorrect, and the opposite is now felt to be the case (Cameron, 1963).

Unfortunately the theoretical inferences drawn from these interesting results are not unequivocal, although the data appear to provide promising evidence for the RNA theory of memory. One of the problems in research involving human subjects is that it is often difficult, impossible, or unethical to run proper drug controls. Evidence will be presented below to indicate that the memory-improving functions of yeast RNA, like those of magnesium pemoline, may be due to a general stimulating or altering effect, and, in this connection one wonders what might have been the results had subjects been given, for example, amphetamine, methylphenidate, or even caffeine. It is possible that in aged, sick, and malnourished patients with impaired metabolic functioning any stimulant might increase performance on "memory" tests through a simple increase in metabolic function and alertness. It should be noted also that Solyom, Enesco, and Beaulieu (1967) present evidence for a differential effect of the injection of yeast RNA both upon metabolism and upon retention performance in rats, depending on the age of the subjects.

It is clear, then, that although Cameron's work is important and potentially relevant to the theoretical issues at hand, the evidence it provides must be regarded as highly circumstantial. Until the proper controls are run, if indeed they can be run, the interpretation of the data must remain very much in doubt.

Research with animals

Because of the control problems inherent in work on yeast RNA injections with human subjects, it was natural for interest to turn to experimentation with animals. Cook, Davidson, Davis, Green, and Fellows (1963) studied the effects of chronic intraperitoneal injections of yeast RNA upon a pole-climbing avoidance response. Animals treated with the RNA solution acquired the response more quickly and showed significantly greater retention after one month than did animals treated with saline. Chronic administration of the drug seemed to be an essential condition of this study, since animals receiving only three days of treatment prior to training did not show the effect in contrast to those receiving RNA for one, two, four or eight weeks.

Wagner, Carder, and Beatty (1966) replicated the Cook et al. study and noted that in all cases the RNA- injected animals made their first avoidance responses much earlier than did the control animals. This resulted in faster acquisition of the response, and the authors note that

> this finding confirms the observation of Cook et al. that yeast RNA injections may facilitate. . .acquisition. . . . It does so, however, without necessarily implicating any improvement in the rats' learning or memory processes.
>
> The control Ss never made the desired response, hence they never experienced the cessation of shock. . . . Each of the RNA injected Ss. . .did make a pole-climbing response during their first several trials and subsequently [responded] . . .more quickly on later trials (p.33).

If a similar enhancement of the probability of the response occurred in the Cook *et al.* study, as Wagner and his co-workers noted, the difference in rates of acquisition might be conceived as being due to differential experience, rather than differential learning ability.

In order to ascertain whether the results obtained by Cook *et al.* might have been due in part to a memory effect, Wagner *et al.* performed a second experiment, comparing RNA- and saline-injected rats on a food-rewarded discrimination task. In this situation stimulation effects of the type suggested by their first experiment would not be facilitatory to performance. No significant differences were found between RNA- and saline-injected animals, although they reported a nonsignificant trend toward faster running speeds in the RNA group. The authors thus concluded that the effect reported by Cook *et al.* seems to be due to some unknown and unspecified factor, which increases the unconditioned probability of a pole-climbing response to shock.

Wagner *et al.* mentioned the possibility that their results might be due to an increase in the general activity level of their RNA-injected rats. They stated that this did not seem likely, since a comparison of mean activity wheel scores of 18 RNA- and 18 saline-injected rats indicated no differences between the groups. However, because they did not describe their method of obtaining these activity measures it is difficult to assess how well they might reflect general activity level. In any case RNA might increase activity level in a manner not amenable to test by the use of activity wheels. Furthermore, the RNA injections might "sensitize" the animal, without increasing activity level.

Recently the Cook group has replicated its earlier findings and placed some limitations upon the interpretation of the prior results (Davidson, Cook, and Davis, 1967). While a full report of this work is not presently available, an abstract states that "the significant part of drug-behavior interaction occurred before or in conjunction with (the) first behavioral response (escape response)" (1967 EPA program, p.122). This result gives added weight to the view that the major effect of RNA injections both here and in the Cook *et al.* (1963) study was on performance and not on learning. It should be mentioned that Cook *et al.* noted this possibility in their 1963 paper, in stating that their results may have been due to an interaction of drug effects with their experimental procedures.

Corson and Enesco (1966) studied the effects of RNA injections upon the behavior of rats in a wide variety of situations. In experiments on spatial and visual discriminations in shock-motivated maze situations no differences were found between RNA- and uric acid-injected (control) animals. A test of open field activity failed to yield differences between groups on activity or reactivity measures. In a fourth experiment, an attempt was made to replicate the experiment of Cook *et al.* (1963), and it was found that RNA animals made fewer errors in acquisition and more responses when shock was no longer being given, suggesting a stimulation effect. In a fifth study it was shown that these results were not a function of strength or endurance differences between the groups.

Corson and Enesco then repeated the four experiments described above, this time using caffeine instead of RNA injections. They cite as their rationale for this procedure those studies which indicate the similarity of effects for RNA in the Skinner box and the T maze to those obtained with central nervous system stimulants. In no case did differences between groups reach statistical significance, and the authors concluded that their results did not support the idea that the effects of RNA injections are comparable to those of CNS stimulants. Again, it should be noted that sensitization effects are not ruled out by these results.

In a last experiment Corson and Enesco tested for differences in water consumption (RNA animals were found to drink less), weight gain (RNA animals were found to gain weight less rapidly), and basal metabolic rate (no differences were found). They concluded that

> while the present results ... in no way exclude the possibility that a memory code may be carried by a special RNA fraction within the cells, they do strongly suggest that the relation of exogenous RNA to memory function is a basically different question from those involving intracellular RNA and problems of information coding in the brain (p. 218).

The work of Corson and Enesco appeared to be evidence for a lack of effect of exogenous RNA, or at least RNA from yeast, upon the processes of learning and memory. Nevertheless, positive results continued to be obtained. In a study reviewed in the section on actinomycin, Batkin et al. (1966) found that RNA, injected intracranially, like actinomycin, improved the performance of carp on a T-maze visual discrimination task. As in the case of their actinomycin data, these investigators interpreted the RNA results in terms of increased availability of free nucleotides from which new, specified RNA might be formed.

Ison and Taplin (1966) used the Hebb-Williams maze, a purported test of problem-solving ability, to investigate the effects of chronic intraperitoneal injections of RNA in rats. The Hebb-Williams (1946) series is designed as a learning set paradigm such that besides studying the ability of animals to learn the 21 individual problems, one may also examine their increasing facility in the solution of this type of problem. In the Ison and Taplin study, rats received daily injections of either RNA or saline solutions during a 31 day adaptation period. For the last 12 days of this period, they were trained on practice problems in the maze, after which the 12 Hebb-Williams series I problems were given, ten trials per problem, one problem per day, with the injection procedure continuing throughout.

Ison and Taplin failed to find a significant difference between groups, but did find a Drug-by-Problem interaction, indicating a weak positive effect on the RNA injections on learning. Furthermore, this difference appeared to correlate with problem difficulty, prompting the authors to suggest that previous failures to obtain effects of RNA injections upon learning may have been due in part to the use of problems which were too simple to discriminate between groups.

They also suggested that the use of the learning set paradigm may be more sensitive to this sort of effect than the use of single problems.

Solyom *et al.* (1967) reported on the effects of RNA injections in old and young rats upon learning and activity. During continuous reinforcement training on a bar press response for water reward, RNA affected the bar press rate only in the old animals. During variable interval training it increased the rate in both groups, with the young animals most affected. RNA inhibited acquisition of a conditioned emotional response in young animals, and appeared to depress activity slightly. On the whole, these results say little about the effects of RNA on learning, but may indicate a mild stimulant effect in the bar press situation. Brown (1966) found a more extreme effect of RNA injections upon bar press rats, using rats of an age intermediate between the two groups of Solyom *et al.*

The data from experiments injecting yeast RNA, therefore, are equivocal, except that a strong tendency toward a stimulant effect has been observed. Before concluding this review, two studies must be mentioned which cast some doubt upon the validity of the entire area. In 1965 Eist and Seal reported that radioactively tagged exogenous RNA failed to pass the blood-brain barrier. This being the case, it seems reasonable to wonder how yeast RNA might be expected to affect learning at all. One possibility, not previously stated in the literature, is that the excess of RNA in the blood might prevent the use of brain RNA outside the brain, thus effectively increasing the amount available for use *in* the brain. Whether this is the case, or indeed whether such uptake of brain RNA by the blood even occurs is unknown.

Cohen and Barondes (1966b) reported that if the reagent grade RNA of the type used in the studies reviewed above was thoroughly purified, it failed to affect performance on a black-white discrimination in the Y-maze. This study further differed from most previous work, including that of Cook *et al.*, in that the authors employed a double-blind procedure. They concluded that in the earlier studies the effects obtained were not due to RNA, but rather to some contaminants in the solutions. It should be noted, however, that Cohen and Barondes employed a very short-term injection regimen. The group receiving the most injections was injected for 13 days prior to training—this length of time is equal to the *shortest* interval shown to be effective in the Cook *et al.* study. Because of this, the validity of Cohen and Barondes' assertion that the earlier effects were most probably due to contaminants is questionable.

Summary of Evidence on RNA

Before describing and evaluating the major theories of RNA as the memory molecule, it would seem well to summarize the evidence presented in this chapter.

From the work on RNA metabolism during behavioral events it seems clear that neural RNA can be strongly influenced by environmental events. In general moderate activity of either sensory or motor cells seems to increase cellular RNA content. Overwork of the cells or inhibition produced by drugs or other agents causes RNA content to decrease. The effect of learning on RNA is not so clear, however. Hydén's work seems to suggest the possibility of changes in RNA base sequences (or at least base ratios) as a result of learning, but procedural difficulties on both the behavioral and the biochemical levels prevent these results from being conclusive.

As for drugs affecting RNA, the case is still less clear. The drugs 8-azaguanine and actinomycin may have a small effect upon memcry and learning through interference with RNA metabolism and synthesis, respectively. In general, the case for 8-azaguanine seems the stronger one. Magnesium pemoline which once seemed so promising now seems to be no more than a stimulant. The initial report of RNA increase through magnesium pemoline, which spurred interest in this drug, now seems to be due to a biochemical artifact. In general, however, the data from work on the first two drugs seem to lead to opposite conclusions, and a definitive experiment is needed.

Yeast RNA seems to act mainly as a stimulant, and even this effect may be due to impurities in the RNA itself. Only Ison and Taplin (1966) indicated any learning effect, and as they pointed out, a wider variety of tasks and task complexity may have to be used to find any effect which exists.

The safest and most parsimonious interpretation of the evidence on RNA at this time seems to be that any role that it plays in memory or learning is not a central one. There are enough unrefuted positive results among the mass of negative evidence to indicate that RNA may have *some* function in learning and memory, but it seems safest at this time to assume that this function is a subsidiary one, in a complex memory system.

Before considering the evidence on protein as the memory molecule, we shall examine the three major theories holding RNA in a central role in memory.

Theories of RNA as the Memory Molecule

As the experimental evidence indicating a memory function for RNA began to accumulate, a number of theories were proposed which assigned a central role to RNA in memory processes. As mentioned above (Chapter II) the early theories rather naïvely assumed that there was a single memory molecule, in this case, RNA. More recently the trend has been toward more complex theorizing. In this section we shall first review Hydén's (1960) early theory, which was one of the first proposed and remains perhaps the best known, despite the fact that Hydén has since abandoned this view in favor of a more complex theory which fits the existing data better. We shall then go on to Landauer's (1964) theory, which may be seen as an extension of Hydén's; it proposes a possible mechanism for the encoding of memory in the RNA molecule. A third major early theory, proposed as an alternative to that of Hydén, takes the phenomenon of enzyme induction (see Chapter III) as its basis. Briggs and Kitto (1962) are the leading proponents of this view. Finally, we shall discuss briefly Hydén's (1967) recent revision of his theory; while this last is not actually on RNA theory, it is most appropriately included here because it springs largely from Hydén's work on RNA and learning as Hydén's earlier theory sprang from his work on RNA and neural stimulation.

Hydén's RNA-specification Theory

Hydén (1960), in an extensive review of nerve cell function and metabolism, proposed a three step process whereby an engram might be laid down. His theory was based on his observation of increased production of nucleoproteins with stimulation (see above) and on the assumptions that nerve cells can readily produce proteins, and that these proteins may be specific.

The three steps in the proposed intracellular mechanism for producing an engram were as follows:

Step 1 is the specification of RNA in the nerve cell by the first series of frequency-coded impulses generated in that neuron in the organism's lifetime. This series of impulses sets up a modulated frequency of electrical discharge which may affect the ionic equilibrium in the cytoplasm. This equilibrium shift, in turn, changes the stability of one or more of the four RNA bases at a site which is dependent upon the particular modulated frequency. This results in an exchange of the now-unstable base for another in the surrounding pool of the cytoplasm, and this site becomes stable for that modulated frequency. The net result of this is an RNA specified for that particular frequency, which is then assumed to remain stable (or, presumably, to be replicated) throughout life.

Step 2 stems from the fact that new RNA and protein are formed in the cell under conditions of neural excitation. Since some of the RNA in the cell is now changed, as described in step one, the protein formed by this RNA will likewise be changed in a manner specific to the RNA and to the frequency specified by the RNA. The second step, therefore, consists of production of a specified protein as a result of the RNA changes which occurred in step one.

Step 3 consists of a rapid dissociation of the specified protein and the complexing of the products of this dissociation with complementary molecules. This complex then activates the neuron's transmitter substance which causes excitation of postsynaptic cells. "The transmitter substance," Hydén notes, "may only facilitate the modulated frequency . . . having a more informative character" when it enters the postsynaptic cell (Hydén, 1960, p. 306).

Once the memory trace is established only step three need take place, giving the dissociation and subsequent release of transmitter substance whenever the particular modulated frequency of input is received.

At face value, Hydén's theory appears to have some merit. Certain flaws, however, are evident. The major flaw is the idea that one cell provides the locus of each memory. The evidence from lesion and brain damage studies is well known and is uniformly against this hypothesis. Hydén attempts to circumvent this problem by proposing that each time a modulated frequency is received not only are already-specified cells activated, but also new cells are specified. While it is true that there are billions of nerve cells in the brain there are also billions of bits of memory stored up in a lifetime, and one wonders how many cells might be allotted to one memory. Since nerve cells do not regenerate and new nerve cells are not formed after birth (Weiss, 1955), this process must seem to be finite.

An argument which is perhaps even more telling against Hydén's theory comes, so to speak, from the other side of the coin. Even if we admit the possibility of one or two cells per memory, it is difficult to conceive that there is only one memory per cell as Hydén's theory implies. Given the respective numbers of bits of information stored and of cells, it would seem necessary for a given cell to have the capability of storing more than one memory trace.

Hydén's theory, however, does have certain positive features. First, there is a certain amount of evidence to support it in Hydén's work (see above). Second, if one takes a longer view, it is possible that Hydén's theory provides a mechanism whereby some other substance might provide the memory trace. If, for example, the specified protein were stored instead of being dissociated, and if it had some capacity to control the firing of the cells, Hydén's first two steps might still hold as the way the engram is set up. As we shall see both in this and in the next chapter there is some basis for believing this to be the case.

One more point should be noted about Hydén's theory, if only in passing. Although it has been considered an "RNA theory" it is easy to see that a slight shift in emphasis would render it liable to be called a "protein theory" of memory as well. It is possible, as we shall see, that what is needed is neither an "RNA" nor a "protein" theory, but rather a hybrid of the two, and as discussed below, Hydén has since adopted this view.

Landauer's Membrane-tuning Theory

In 1964 Landauer noted that most theories of the biochemical basis of memory have in common one factor. In most of these theories there are first specific changes in RNA of certain cells and then these changes give rise to (or change the probability of) certain behaviors. Landauer noted that this involves the two processes of learning and retrieval and proposed two hypotheses concerning the mechanisms involved.

Landauer's learning hypothesis is based upon the fact that the optimal CS-UCS interval in classical conditioning is appreciably greater than 0 and for different response systems may vary from 0.45 secs. to even longer intervals (Jones, 1962). This implies that some sequential activity is involved in the learning processes of the brain. He proposed that the new RNA, specified for the CS (csRNA), might be produced in the glia for a period of time following the presentation of the CS. If the characteristics of glia-neuron interchanges of RNA were such that this csRNA could then enter only those cells conducting impulses at the end of this period, then these neurons involved in reception of the UCS would gain new, specified RNA. If, in turn, this csRNA resulted in an increased probability of firing of this cell to the next CS, then conditioning would have occurred. The mechanics of the system are illustrated in Figure 6, where the temporal relations between the various processes are shown. Glial csRNA production proceeds during the CS-UCS interval. At the onset of the UCS, csRNA passes from the glia into the neuron, where it is stored.

In reading Landauer's theory one first notes the neatness of the system and then its biggest difficulty. It is well known (Ochs, 1966) that the permeability of the plasma membrane to large molecules is very low. It is difficult, therefore, to conceive of a situation wherein large quantities of RNA could pass into the cell. Landauer acknowledged this, but stated that there are cases where large molecules do cross, and in the course of the great changes in the electrochemical characteristics of the membrane which take place during impulse conduction it is not inconceivable that this might occur. In fact, Landauer worked out a mathematical proof of this based on the electrophoretic mobility of RNA and the charge gradients set up in impulse conduction. The computations of this proof are beyond the scope of this review, but suffice to say that it showed that there is more than adequate energy available for such a large-scale transfer to occur.

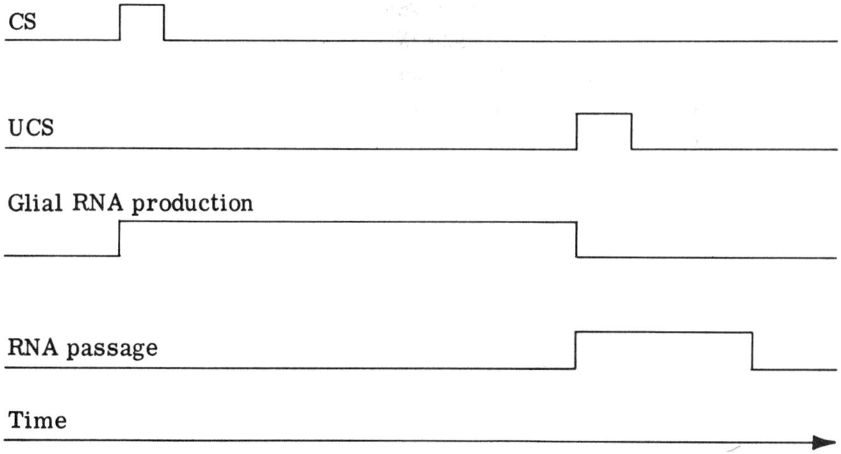

Fig. 6: *Temporal relations of Landauer's theory.*

Landauer's second hypothesis is concerned with retrieval of stored information. The first hypothesis departed from traditional views in that conditioning was seen as consisting not of increased synaptic conductance between neurons but as a change in the sensitivity of many individual neurons to some aspect of the brain activity involved in CS reception. The second hypothesis went on to state that if the neural membrane is seen as a narrow pass-band filter, then the currents which spread from a given neuron into the surrounding tissue during conduction will have certain characteristic frequency patterns. These spreading currents will then affect certain other neurons having similar or identical pass-band characteristics.

Retrieval, then, comes about due to the fact that the tuning of a membrane is determined by its constituent proteins. The passage of RNA from glia to neuron would change the "tuning" of the filter due to altered aspects of RNA-dependent protein synthesis, and would change it such that it would more probably fire to the CS. Since this neuron was originally involved in UCS reception, stimulus substitution would have occurred and learning would be complete.

As Landauer noted, these are hypotheses and are not yet well founded in research. The work of Hydén's group, however, agrees well with some of Landauer's views. For example Hydén has shown that during neural activity glial RNA decreases and neuronal RNA increases, as would be expected from Landauer's theory. Furthermore, as Landauer noted, the data of Hydén and Egyházi and Hydén and Lange (q.v. supra) on RNA changes might indicate incorporation into the neurons of novel RNA, but it should be noted that Hydén has only shown the glial RNA decreases and neuronal RNA increases during stimulation. He has never shown this to be the case during learning, and so any support for Landauer's theory from Hydén's work is inferential rather than direct.

In that area of his theory where he departs most radically from accepted views Landauer is also most lacking in empirical support. The mechanism of chemical rearrangement shown in Figure 6 could allow for changes in the synapse, as postulated by the classical theories (Chapter I), and could take place through enzyme induction in line with modern theorizing (see below). Furthermore, the incorporation of new chemicals by electrophoresis could provide the mechanism by which synaptic resistance is lowered only between selected neurons. Not content with these older views, however, Landauer suggested the idea of conditioning as a change in selective sensitivity of single neurons. This notion, while an intriguing one, is wholly lacking in empirical basis, and is, rather, pure speculation. A more important criticism of Landauer's theory asks whether it is, indeed, a theory at all. Landauer himself did not style it so, referring throughout his 1964 paper to his "two hypotheses." It is clear, however, that a theory is being proposed. Grossman (1967) places these 2 hypotheses on a par with the theories of Hydén, Gaito, and others. One feels, however, that Landauer's hypotheses are less a theory than a mechanism. What Landauer appears to have done is to set up a fairly plausible, although perhaps only partially testable, set of operations which might provide a mechanism for the changes proposed by Hydén in his early theory. Indeed throughout his paper Landauer notes how well his model fits the data of Hydén's group, as it clearly does. Landauer's paper, therefore, proposes not a unified theory but rather a mechanism to fill in the biochemical gaps in Hydén's theory.

Briggs and Kitto's Enzyme-induction Theory

This type of theory has been gaining in popularity steadily over the past five years or so, and has recently achieved a great deal of importance in the work of Flexner (see Chapter VI). Since Flexner proposed a protein-oriented enzyme-induction theory, we will postpone discussion of his view until the next chapter. Briggs and Kitto (1962) proposed that memory might be based in the concentrations of certain enzymes in neural tissue, and that RNA changes might be simply a reflection of these concentration changes. The enzymes they considered most likely were those involved in the manufacture and breakdown of the neural transmitter substances, especially acetylcholine. Because of the involvement of RNA in protein (enzyme) metabolism, changes in enzyme concentration would be reflected in changes in RNA.

Smith (1962) reviewed Briggs and Kitto's theory and applied it to show how repeated stimulation of a nerve path might cause increased conductance of this path via induction of the enzymes of the ACh system. Actually, most of the discussion of Briggs and Kitto's theory has been of this type with very little direct experimental test.

Grossman (1967) reviews the secondary evidence relating to the theory, and concludes that it has a great deal of indirect support derived mainly from inferences from the work reviewed in the first section of this chapter and from the work of Krech's group (see Chapter II). Flexner, Flexner, and Roberts (1967), to be discussed below, noted that this *sort* of theory appears to be a likely candidate for the correct one, although Flexner's work indicates that it is his, and not Briggs and Kitto's theory, which holds the highest probability of verification.

Hydén's "DNA Activation" Theory

Hydén's early (1960) theory, reviewed above, was based largely on his pre-1962 experiments in which he studied the effects on RNA of sensory and chemical stimulation. As his research progressed, in the mid 1960's, through learning experiments (see above), Hydén found it necessary to revise his theory to fit both his data and those of others which indicated something less than a central role for RNA in memory. Hydén's new theory is not yet fully developed, and in his most recent statement of it (Hydén, 1967) he characterizes it as a "working hypothesis." We shall briefly review it here as an example of the recent trend toward the RNA-DNA-protein complex type of theory.

Hydén (1967) stresses in the statement of his theory that there is no evidence to support a mechanistic model of simple "taping" of molecules for memory storage. He feels that the system must be far more complex than this, and must involve the cells'genetic apparatus. However, as Hydén points out, only a small portion of the genetic apparatus is active in the mature cell, and so it might be difficult to postulate a use for this apparatus. Hydén circumvents this problem by stating that *because* only a small part of the genome is active, it would only be necessary to activate a very small additional portion in order to obtain a high degree of specificity.

Briefly described, Hydén's theory has three stages. In the first, the reception of sensory information by the appropriate brain areas causes an activation of certain genomes in the cells of these areas (DNA activation), resulting in the production of new, specified mRNA. Hydén (1967) cites recent evidence indicating that this is a plausible hypothesis.

In the second stage, the RNA synthesis of the first stage causes the production of new protein, which facilitates the transmission of the patterns of sensory input from one neuron to another, thus setting up a series of neurons which are coded for this input. This facilitation of transmission occurs via an interaction between the specified protein and the neural transmitter substance of the cell.

The third stage of Hydén's theory consists of the maintenance of the cellular changes by the specified protein.

This summary of Hydén's theory is, of course, highly simplified. Hydén (1967) cites a great deal of supporting evidence, both empirical and logical, which has not been presented here, and he also goes into greater detail on each of the points mentioned. The theory fits well with existing data, and seems quite liable to experimental test. It is this sort of theory, taken together with the type of theory proposed by Flexner (see Chapter VI) which most probably will ultimately prove of the greatest value in determining the chemical basis of memory.

Summary of RNA as the Memory Molecule

We have seen that the data relating to RNA as the memory molecule are tenuous and lead to the conclusion that, while RNA is probably involved, it is most likely *not* the sole basis of memory. In our review of the theories on RNA, we have seen that these theories which have found any prominence at all assign a subordinate role to RNA. In the next two chapters we shall see that the evidence on protein as the memory substrate, while not unequivocal, is more favorable, and that there is some evidence from studies using inter-animal transfer of learning, and RNAse controls, that RNA does not hold a central role.

chapter
VI

PROTEIN AS THE
MEMORY MOLECULE

Katz and Halstead (1950) proposed a theory of memory which assigned a central role to protein as the chemical basis of memory. The theory received little notice at the time because, as Gaito (1966) points out, the *Zeitgeist* in psychology was not ready for the relatively sophisticated biochemical thinking involved. In more recent years the fact that a basic genetic assumption of the theory was proved to be in error has led to a general neglect of the theory even though many of its aspects remain sound (Grossman, 1967).

As we have seen in the preceding chapters, interest in recent years has centered around the nucleic acids, especially RNA, as possible memory molecules. It is only very recently, with the accumulation of negative and equivocal evidence on RNA, that interest has once again turned toward protein. (As we have noted, theorizing about individual molecules is becoming outmoded in favor of the DNA-RNA-protein complex type of theory. The division along molecular lines, however, has been and continues to be a convenient simplification for purposes of basic research and theorizing.) The experimental evidence favoring the protein hypothesis has come largely from two sources, work with drugs and inter-animal transfer studies. This chapter will be concerned with the first of these and with the major protein-based theories of memory. Discussion of inter-animal transfer work will be deferred to the next chapter.

Research with TCAP

Hydén and Hartelius (1948) published an extensive study of the effects of injections of the drug malononitrile $(CH_2[CN]_2)$ on cell chemistry and mental disorders. The major findings of this study were that the drug (1) greatly increased synthesis of nucleo-proteins in nerve cells, and (2) caused a remission of symptoms in a number of psychological disorders in hospitalized patients. These authors interpreted the results to indicate a link between protein and mental function, thus anticipating the more extensive theorizing of Katz and Halstead (1950).

Prompted by a failure to replicate Hydén and Hartelius' findings, Mendelson, Mendelson, Fax, and Grenell (1954) performed chemical analyses on the type of malononitrile solution used by Hydén and Hartelius. They discovered that the substance injected by these investigators contained not only malononitrile, but also an aging product of the drug, and ascribed the results of Hydén and Hartelius' study to the presence of this contaminant. Eberts (1960) subsequently identified this aging product as a dimerized form of malononitrile, characterized as 1,1,3-tricyano-2-amino-1-propene, the structure of which is shown in Figure 7. Eberts concluded that prior work with malononitrile solutions should be re-evaluated because the extent of contamination was unknown. Since 1960 the dimer has been used in research as a drug distinct from malononitrile, and Hydén and Hartelius' (1948) results have generally been ascribed to its presence. The drug is most commonly called TCAP although it has been designated variously U-9189 (Upjohn), tricyanoaminopropene, tri-a-p, and simply malononitrile dimer.

Fig. 7: *Structure of 1,1,3-tricyano-2-amino-1-propene.*

Egyházi and Hydén (1961) investigated the effects of TCAP upon neuronal and glial production of RNA and protein, and found results similar to those reported by Hydén and Hartelius (1948) using impure malononitrile. It should be noted here that although most investigators have used TCAP as an aid in the study of the effects of alterations in RNA metabolism upon learning, there is no *a priori* justification for considering the effective action of the drug to be on RNA alone. The results of these two studies show effects both on RNA and on protein metabolism, with, in fact, the effect on protein synthesis somewhat stronger than that on RNA synthesis. Thus all positive effects of TCAP may be interpreted as favoring a protein hypothesis rather than the RNA hypothesis (or, better perhaps, as a result of the joint action of the drug on RNA *and* protein).

Chamberlain *et al.* (1963) investigated the effects of TCAP on spinal cord fixation (a technique discussed on page 31 above), avoidance conditioning, and Hebb-Williams maze learning. Injections of TCAP shortened spinal cord fixation time from 45 minutes (controls) to 30 minutes, and TCAP-treated animals were also superior to controls in avoidance conditioning. No differences were found in the Hebb-Williams test, as was the case with 8-azaguanine. Chamberlain *et al.* interpreted the TCAP results as favoring an RNA theory of learning, but, as noted above, the protein interpretation would serve equally well.

Essman (1966) investigated the effects of three daily TCAP injections on ECS-induced amnesia in mice. Animals were trained in a one-trial passive avoidance paradigm and then given a single ECS. In retention testing after 24 hours, control animals showed the characteristic amnesia for the avoidance response, but TCAP-injected animals showed significant retention. A later study in Essman's laboratory (Lewis, 1967) investigated the effects of long series of injections of TCAP and a second malononitrile derivative, tetracyanoaminopropene (designated T4CAP) on maze learning in rats. The second compound, a malononitrile trimer, had not been used previously in any published study. Lewis found that this drug elevated brain RNA and protein levels in a manner similar to that of TCAP. In a series of experiments on acquisition of a water maze task by mice Lewis found that if motor training was given prior to the inception of drug administration, both TCAP and T4CAP facilitated maze learning, with T4CAP somewhat more effective. Without prior motor training only high doses of T4CAP affected maze learning. Lewis interpreted these results as evidence for an effect of the two drugs on learning at the choice point rather than on motor learning.

Brush, Davenport and Polidora (1966) investigated the effects of TCAP on learning in two situations. These were an avoidance conditioning task similar to that of Chamberlain *et al.* (1963) and a water maze task similar to that used by Lewis (1967). In the avoidance conditioning experiment rats were trained for two or three days post-injection, 30 trials per day. No differences on number of avoidance responses, latency of responding, or number of intertrial responses were found between drug- and placebo-injected animals for any of the training days. It is important to note that Brush *et al.* used single injections of TCAP, whereas Lewis used a multiple injections technique.

In the maze-learning experiment animals were given pretraining in the straight runway followed by three days of maze training and two days of maze reversal training. In addition, some animals were tested for retention after 9 and 40 days. No significant differences were found between drug and control animals on speed or error scores. Brush *et al.* stated that the discrepancy between their avoidance conditioning results and those of Chamberlain *et al.* (1963) might be due to certain procedural differences between the two studies, although this is ". . . not readily understandable" (p. 184). They asserted, however, that the differences between the water maze procedures might be sufficient to produce the discrepant results. Brush *et al.* concluded tentatively that the most important factor in the effectiveness of TCAP as an aid to learning might be the duration of drug treatment — chronic administration seems to give facilitation of learning, whereas acute administration does not.

In a study of the effect of TCAP on learning in aged white rats, Solyom and Gallay (1966) reported that the drug significantly increased response output in the Skinner box during training on a variable interval schedule, but did not affect acquisition or extinction of a CER. The authors concluded that although these results might be due to better learning of the bar press response, it is more likely that they reflect a stimulant function for the drug. This conclusion, however, seems equally implausible since a stimulant effect would be expected to appear as heightened responding during CER training, a result which was not obtained.

A recent study by Gurowitz, Gross, and George (1968) investigated the effects of several doses of TCAP on learning in the passive avoidance (PAR) situation. Doses used were 15, 30, and 45 mg/kg, the last being a higher dose than has commonly been used. All three doses of the drug were found to disrupt passive avoidance learning, *i.e.,* all three doses had a stimulant effect. The authors concluded that while acute administration of the drug does not seem to affect learning, the results of Essman (1966) and Lewis (1967) indicate that chronic administration may be necessary to obtain facilitatory effects.

To summarize, the research on TCAP, while not wholly unequivocal, does seem to indicate some effect of the drug on learning. Because TCAP affects both RNA and protein metabolism it is difficult to be certain of the effective location of action, but in the light of other data (reviewed below and in Chapter VII) the function of protein in memory coding seems underrated by current investigators using the drug.

Research with Puromycin

Research investigating the effects of puromycin injections on learning has come primarily from Flexner's laboratory at the University of Pennsylvania. The very few other studies that have been done (*e.g.,* Barondes and Cohen, 1966; Davis and Agranoff, 1966) have generally confirmed the work of Flexner's group. This section, therefore, will comprise a detailed discussion of Flexner's work.

Flexner and his colleagues began, in 1962, a series of investigations to study the effects of the antibiotic puromycin on learning and memory. Earlier, Yarmolinsky and de la Haba (1959) had shown that it inhibited protein synthesis through competitive interaction for the amino acid-bearing sites on mRNA. All of Flexner's experiments make use of the same behavioral situation (Flexner *et al.,* 1967). Mice are trained in a Y maze to avoid shock by selecting the proper arm of the maze to a criterion of 9 correct responses out of 10, using a correction procedure. In retention testing errors are punished by shock.

In the first experiments (Flexner, Flexner, Stellar, de la Haba, and Roberts, 1962), puromycin was administered subcutaneously in the highest dose (0.42 mg/g) which the mice could tolerate. Inhibition of protein synthesis (measured as uptake of administered radioactive valine) was virtually complete (~90%) in all non-neural tissues studied within one hour. (Cerebral cortex inhibition took two hours, and was less complete—~80%). No behavioral effects of these injections were observed, and so intracranial administration (Flexner, Flexner, and Steller, 1963) was turned to as a method of obtaining greater degrees of inhibition. Three types of intracranial injection were devised, and experiments were performed using each type separately and in combination. One type, frontal injection (F), was shown by fluorescein tracing to cover the rostral third of the cerebral cortex; the second, ventricular injection (V), covered all of the hippocampus and the caudal half of the neocortex; the third, temporal injection (T), covered the hippocampus, the caudal third of the neocortex, and all of the temporal and entorhinal cortices. Flexner (1966) reported that the staining of F+T+V injections was essentially the sum· of that for the three injections separately, and that this additive effect also applied to combinations of two injections.

The first behavioral studies using these methods (Flexner et al., 1963) were done on mice trained to criterion on the Y-maze discrimination task and injected one day later. After F+T+V injections (30-60 μg/mouse), retention for the training experience was completely lost. The most consistent memory loss with localized injections occurred with temporal injections (90 μg). Frontal or ventricular, or combinations of these, were "essentially without effect" (Flexner, 1966, p. 10).

Subsequently, Flexner et al. (1963) investigated what they termed "longer term memory," as opposed to the "short-term memory" tests described above. Here mice were trained to criterion and injected with puromycin 11-43 days later. In this case, only F+T+V injections were consistently effective in destroying memory and all single or double-combination injections were without effect. From this Flexner (1966) concluded that

> There was consequently a clear distinction between recent and longer-term memory. Recent memory was lost when puromycin was introduced through temporal injections to involve ... the hippocampi and caudal cortices, including the temporal cortices ..., while loss of longer-term memory required puromycin ... in a substantially greater part of the neocortex (p.11).

Unfortunately the anatomical boundaries cannot at this time be made any more specific than this, first because it is difficult to confine intracerebral injections within anatomical boundaries, and second because, as Flexner (1966) pointed out, the actual spread of the puromycin, as measured by biochemical techniques, was greater than was indicated by ultra-violet measurement of the fluorescein spread.

Flexner et al. (1963) extended this time-course effect by training a group of mice to criterion on the Y-maze discrimination task, and then three weeks later giving them reversal training. The point under investigation here was whether it was possible "to destroy memory of reversal learning 24 hours after reversal training and spare the longer-term memory of the initial training" (Flexner, 1966, p. 12).

To test this, 7 animals were given bilateral T injections 24 hours after reversal training. In retention trials (given 3 days after injection) shock was omitted, since in this case there was no "correct" response possible. In all 7 animals their first choice was consistent with the initial (pre-reversal) training, as were the majority of subsequent choices.

In a recent paper (Flexner, Flexner, and Roberts, 1967) further observations of the effects of puromycin were reported. First, it was noted that in mice trained just to criterion both recent and long-term memory are maintained for 10 to 20 hours after injection of puromycin before loss of memory. Testing for up to a three month period indicated that the subsequent loss was permanent. Second, it was found that overtraining protected the memory against attack by puromycin. They found that an average of 60 trials was needed to obtain protection. Third, they noted that mice which had received puromycin treatment were able to relearn the maze and were capable of reversal learning. This new learning was retained indefinitely. It is interesting that speed of learning on second training matched very closely that on first training in many (but not all) of the mice. This would seem to indicate that while the disruptive effect of puromycin on specific memories is permanent there may be no lasting effect upon the memory system *per se*.

In the conclusion of a review of his research, Flexner (1966) considered the question of whether this evidence allows the conclusion that memory for simple maze learning in the mouse depends on continuing synthesis of protein. He stated that

> our position is [not] sufficiently secure to make this statement with confidence. There is . . . nothing . . . to contradict it. But all our positive results . . . have been obtained with puromycin which might well have some other effect . . . spuriously related to its effect on protein synthesis (p. 19)

Flexner went on to state (1966, p. 19) that it would be desirable to obtain data on another substance which produced inhibition of protein synthesis by a different mechanism, but was similar to puromycin in other aspects such as extent and time course of the inhibition. Such data would provide a valuable comparison to determine whether the memory effects were due to the protein inhibition alone or to interference with some larger chemical system.

Recently, Flexner has begun an investigation of the effects of the antibiotic acetoxycycloheximide (Flexner et al., 1967). This drug fulfills the requirements discussed above for a comparison medium because it is a powerful inhibitor of protein synthesis but does so through a mechanism different from that of puromycin. Flexner et al. stated that if this drug would similarly have a deleterious effect upon memory, then the view that memory depends upon protein alone would receive support.

Behavioral results obtained with the heximide indicated that the maintenance of protein synthesis alone is not a sufficient condition for memory storage. Despite the profound depression of protein synthesis by this drug, memory was impaired only briefly, after which it returned to normal. Flexner et al. (1967)

proposed two possible explanations for this difference between puromycin and acetoxycycloheximide. First, the heximide, in addition to blocking protein synthesis, might prevent protein breakdown. This would eliminate the necessity for continued synthesis to maintain the level of protein needed for memory. Second, there is the possibility that memory is partly dependent on mRNA produced during learning. Flexner *et al.* stated that with puromycin, RNA is degraded normally but without replacement, whereas the heximide decreases the rate of RNA decay. The theoretical basis for this second hypothesis will become clearer in our discussion of Flexner's theory (q.v. infra).

If the second of these hypotheses is correct, then the effect of puromycin on memory would be expected to be reduced if puromycin were given jointly with acetoxycycloheximide (Flexner *et al.*, 1967). When this was done memory was found to be protected against the effects of puromycin. In addition, other antibiotics which, like acetoxycyloheximide, interfere with peptide bond formation and depress RNA degradation, were found to have a similar effect.

Two recent studies by Barondes and Cohen (1967a, b) provide interesting data on the effects of acetoxycycloheximide on memory. These authors pointed out that puromycin produces certain abnormalities of cerebral electrical activity, while the heximide does not (Cohen, Ervin, and Barondes, 1966), which led them to state that interpretation of the results of Flexner's group using puromycin is difficult. In their first study, Barondes and Cohen (1967a) compared the effects of intracerebral injections of puromycin and cycloheximide on learning and retention of an avoidance task in mice. Cycloheximide is a potent inhibitor of brain protein synthesis, and for our purposes may be considered to be the same as acetoxycycloheximide. They found that while puromycin-injected mice were unable to learn the avoidance problem, cycloheximide-injected mice learned and retained it quite well. Thus, despite the fact that the brains of heximide-treated mice showed the greater degree of protein synthesis impairment, Barondes and Cohen concluded that these results were not in accord with the theory that continued protein synthesis is necessary for consolidation of memory.

In their second study, Barondes and Cohen (1967b) noted that all the studies on the effects of these protein inhibitors in mice gave what they termed "prolonged training" despite the fact that mice learned to solve the problem in a relatively small number of trials. In other words, animals were overtrained, which might make it difficult to detect interference with memory by the drugs. In this study, Barondes and Cohen ran their animals to one of two criteria: nine correct responses out of ten consecutive trials (prolonged training), or three out of four (brief training). Acetoxycycloheximide was injected prior to training, as in the previous work. In those animals receiving brief training it was found that retention was normal at three hours after training, but at six hours and thereafter there was a marked impairment in retention. In those animals receiving prolonged training, however, no impairment was seen even after several days and with very high doses of the drug.

These results are in accord with Barondes' and Cohen's earlier view that learning and consolidation are not dependent on cerebral protein synthesis. However, they were now able to conclude that a separate long-term memory process apparently *is* dependent on such synthesis. It should be noted that these authors reported that this "long-term memory disruption" is not easily demonstrable — it is offset by overtraining, and is apparently dependent upon nearly total inhibition of protein synthesis (95% or greater). They proposed that protein synthesis may be needed to produce the conditions necessary for the translation of short-term (non-consolidated) memory into stable (long-term) memory.

It is interesting to note in passing that this may explain why acute administration of TCAP (above) is not effective in facilitating learning and retention while chronic administration appears to be. It may be that long-term injections are needed to raise levels of protein synthesis to the point where they are sustained enough to last through the consolidation phase.

The work with puromycin and acetoxycycloheximide provides what is perhaps the clearest evidence we have seen with regard to the molecular substrate of learning and memory. The evidence seems unequivocal that continued protein synthesis during and for a time after learning is a necessary condition for the laying down of a long-lasting memory trace. Additionally, RNA seems involved insofar as intact RNA metabolism seems to be a further necessary condition. After a brief review of Katz and Halstead's (1950) historic theory, we shall examine Flexner's attempt to bring together his data on puromycin and memory into a theory of the chemical basis of memory.

Theories of Protein as the Memory Molecule

The evidence from puromycin and TCAP studies suggests a central role for protein in memory. The beginnings of further support are found in the experiment of Caldwell and Churchill (1967) in which pregnant rats deprived of protein in the second half of gestation produced progeny severely deficient in maze learning ability. These results suggest the question of the mechanism whereby protein might encode and store memory. Two theories have been advanced which propose a central role for protein in memory.

Katz and Halstead's Nucleoprotein Theory

Katz and Halstead's (1950) theory, as we have noted, has received relatively little attention, partly because of a fundamental error in its assumptions. It remains, however, a valuable example of how relatively sophisticated biochemical thinking can be applied to behavioral problems. Additionally it has historical value as the first systematic theory of the chemical basis of memory. They based their theory on the analogy between genetics and memory (q.v. supra p. 35). At the time of their work it was generally assumed that each gene was composed of one nucleoprotein molecule, and so it was natural for Katz and Halstead to attempt to apply the same system to individual memory. They asserted that memory might consist of the formation of new protein molecules in central nervous system neurons. These new molecules would encode memory in the way genes encode hereditary information, and would, presumably, read out memory in an analogous manner.

They went on to suggest that the new molecules of various cells extend from one cell to the next to form protein latticeworks, and it is these latticeworks that actually constitute the memory trace. Katz and Halstead conceived of a neuron as inactive until it became part of a neural network through construction of a lattice. Different memory traces were thought to be distinguished from each other by the chemical structure of their lattices.

Katz and Halstead believed that the unorganized neuron was incapable of impulse conduction, and contained a random array of protein molecules. The first impulse to come to the neuron caused a rearrangement of this random protein into an ordered array whereupon the neuron could subsequently conduct impulses. Once the first neuron of a network was organized the organization spread to an adjacent neuron, by some unknown mechanism. This process of propagation was felt to continue through the cortex until it encountered an already-organized neuron or one deficient in the protein being organized. Katz and Halstead pointed out that memory traces might not be so linear as is implied by this description, but rather might spread in several directions from a common point. Also, various traces would set up interrelationships based on common chemical characteristics.

Katz and Halstead were incorrect in their basic assumption and unfounded in some of their further ones. It is interesting to note, however, that although most subsequent theories have involved protein changes to some extent, it was not until very recently that any other theorists have even attempted to propose a mechanism for these changes. The mechanism proposed by Katz and Halstead was based on the "core conductor" view of the neuron, and considered the membrane to be a semiconductor. The steps involved in the development of the model are beyond the scope of this paper and can be found in the Katz and Halstead (1950) monograph.

Katz and Halstead's theory is largely untestable experimentally, and so has little value as a theory of memory. It remains, however, the first attempt at a molecular view of memory processes.

Flexner's "Self-inducing System" Theory

In the review of the work with puromycin and acetoxycycloheximide (v. supra) evidence was presented indicating that memory might be dependent upon two factors: (a) continued protein synthesis and (b) preservation of mRNA, as indicated by the depression of mRNA decay by acetoxycycloheximide. In

Flexner's theory (Flexner *et al.*, 1967) long-term memory is dependent not on the continued presence of any particular protein or nucleic acid molecule, but on the establishment of a self-sustaining system for their maintenance.

The process proposed by Flexner is analogous to the phenomenon of gene repression. When the products of a gene's expression act as inducers (derepressors) of that gene, a self-sustaining system is set up (this constitutes DNA derepression, as in the theories of Hydén [1967] and Gaito [1966b], described above). If the gene is repressed, inducers are not synthesized and the gene remains in a repressed state. Conversely, if the gene is induced for a sufficient time the inducers will accumulate above a critical level and the gene will remain in the induced state unless synthetic processes are inhibited and the reserve of inducers is used up (Flexner *et al.*, 1967). A similar self-inducing system is applied to learning in Flexner's theory.

We assume that the initial learning experience triggers the synthesis of one or more species of mRNA. This mRNA alters the synthetic rate of one or more proteins which are essential for the expression of memory. These proteins are thought to modify the characteristics of synapses concerned in a learning process so that the passage of impulses between nerve cells is facilitated. In turn, the proteins or their products act as inducers of their related mRNA (Flexner *et al.*, 1967, p. 1382).[1]

Thus, loss of the mRNA would lead to loss of the protein and permanent loss of memory, as was seen to be the case in research with puromycin. If protein synthesis were depressed but mRNA conserved, as with acetoxycycloheximide, loss of memory would be temporary. This temporary memory loss with acetoxycycloheximide has been reported (Flexner, Flexner, and Roberts, 1966).

As Flexner *et al.* (1967) point out, only a beginning has been made in testing the self-inducing system theory experimentally. It is important to note, however, that all of the data accrued to date have been favorable to this view. Further, the theory is in accord with the results of Hydén's group (Hydén and Egyházi, 1964; Hydén and Lange, 1965) reporting increases in nuclear RNA following training, and with the recent work of Zemp, Wilson, Schlesinger, Boggan, and Glassman (1966) demonstrating increased synthesis of nuclear RNA during learning.

Summary of Protein as the Memory Molecule

Research on protein as a possible memory substrate appears to show the greatest probability of success of any of the research reviewed in the last three chapters. This is especially true when the research reviewed in this chapter is taken together with the results of studies of inter-animal transfer of training, which will be reviewed in the next chapter. This work originally showed promise for the RNA theories but now appears to support the protein view.

[1] Copyright 1967, American Association for the Advancement of Science.

chapter
VII

STUDIES
OF INTER-ANIMAL
TRANSFER
OF LEARNING

Given the premise that memory storage involves the establishment of a chemical trace, it might be possible to extract this trace unharmed and implant it in a recipient[1] animal in a manner analogous to the way that organs are donated and received. Work on inter-animal transfer of learning has taken two main lines. First, work has been done with the planarian *Dugesia* on inter- and intra-animal transfer. Second, more extensive research has been done recently on inter-animal transfer in mammals, generally rats or mice. In the latter case two methods are used: (a) extraction of a single substance, *e.g.*, RNA, from donor brains and its injection into recipients and (b) homogenization of entire donor brains, and subsequent injection of the homogenates into recipients.

The research done on inter-animal transfer, especially that using mammalian species, has yielded results which are often contradictory and always complex. This review will not stay closely with chronological order, but rather will attempt to present the studies in such an order as to indicate which results seem to represent real effects, and which seem to be unreplicable or due to some methodological artifact.

Research with *Planaria*[2]

Much of the research on learning in *Planaria* has been done by a group of investigators headed by McConnell (see McConnell, 1962). Experiments with

[1] In this chapter the term "donor" will refer to trained or naïve animals sacrificed to provide material for injection into other animals, designated "recipients".

[2] As McConnell kindly pointed out (personal communication) the plural of planarian is planarians. The term *Planaria* is a generic term. I mention this because of the common error of using planaria for the plural of planarian.

these organisms are of two types, both of which are relevant to the subject of this review. The first type of experiment involves intra-animal rather than inter-animal transfer. It entails transecting the planarian, allowing regeneration to take place, and testing for retention of previously conditioned response. The second type of experiment deals with true inter-animal transfer through ingestion of trained donors by naïve recipients.

Intra-animal Transfer

The first study of retention following regeneration was carried out by McConnell, Jacobson, and Kimble (1959). These experimenters trained planarians in a classical conditioning procedure, then cut them across the middle and allowed them to regenerate fully. This yielded two animals for every one conditioned. The regenerates were then retrained to assess savings. Control groups consisted of naïve regenerates trained at the same interval after being cut, and uncut worms trained and then tested for retention after a month to control for decay of retention. Experimental animals (regenerates) showed retention equal to that of uncut controls, regardless of whether the regenerate came from a "tail" or "head" half.

Some supportive evidence indicating that memory storage in the planarian might indeed be chemical was provided by an experiment by Corning and John (1961). These investigators reasoned that in planarians regenerated from tail-halves, memory of the conditioned response might be expected to be passed from the tail end to the regenerated head end. This is a reasonable expectation in view of the fact that planarians do show a degree of cephalic dominance. Corning and John felt that RNA might play a role in the transmission of a chemically stored memory from trained to regenerated tissue. Thus conditioned tails regenerating in a ribonuclease (RNAse) medium might produce heads which were deficient in RNA, and hence naïve with respect to the prior training of the tail. In the case of trained heads, however, a greater degree of retention might be expected, since only a non-dominant tail is regenerated.

Corning and John trained planarians in a classical conditioning procedure involving paired light and shock. Their design consisted of two experimental groups, one regenerated in RNAse and the other in pond water. In addition, they ran eight control groups to control for factors such as sensitization due to RNAse, time elapsed between training and testing, and effect of RNAse on training the animals, cutting them, and allowing 14 to 18 days for regeneration to take place. Animals were then tested for retention, retrained, and again tested for retention.

Corning and John's results indicated that regeneration in RNAse (as contrasted with water) does not affect acquisition (relearning) adversely. Furthermore, transection alone does not interfere with acquisition or retention, nor were there time course effects. The data further indicated that while learning and retention of head halves regenerated in RNAse were not affected, tail halves regenerated in this way were severely deficient in retention of the CR, although they did show some savings in retraining.

The results of Corning and John's study appear to provide evidence consistent with chemical storage of memory in the planarian by RNA. However, caution must be exercised in the interpretation of these results because of an irregularity in the statistical analysis employed. In their paper Corning and John report only the results of those t-tests which reached significance ($P < .05$). While they do not report how many t-tests they ran overall, it appears that they compared all combinations of groups, conditions, and stages of training for a total of 148 t-tests, of which 14, or 9.5%, yielded significant results. Although Corning and John indicated that some comparisons were critical and others were not expected to yield a difference, it is impossible to state which of the significant results represent true effects and which are part of those which would be expected to exceed significance by chance alone. To ascertain this would require a replication making only those comparisons which proved significant to see which if any represent replicable effects. More important evidence against the wholehearted acceptance of Corning and John's results comes from the work of Halas, to be discussed below.

Inter-animal transfer

Besides working with the sort of intra-animal transfer procedures we have been discussing, investigators have also attempted to transfer memory from one planarian to another through ingestion. This procedure involves training a donor worm, chopping this donor into small pieces, and feeding it to an untrained recipient worm. McConnell (1962) noted that

> since planarians have but the most rudimentary of digestive tracts, there seemed an excellent chance that the tissue from the food worm would pass into the body of the cannibal relatively unchanged (p. 48).

McConnell (1962) cited a series of studies in which this procedure was used with the added precaution of the use of a "blind" running technique, wherein the experimenter is unaware of the group identity of the animals he is running. This procedure was not used in the earlier work on regeneration. In all of these studies, recipients of material from trained donors performed at or near the criterion of learning from the first day of training, while control animals (recipients from naïve donors) took several days to reach this level. McConnell (1962) interpreted these results as evidence of a chemical basis for memory in *Planaria*, speculating on the possibility of extracting specific chemical substances from the donor tissue before feeding it to recipients in order to further delineate the nature of this chemical substrate.

An important factor which must be considered in the discussion of work with *Planaria* is the possibility of errors in response detection (Rosenthal, 1963).

In work with an organism of this size, it would seem likely that the experimenter's expectancies might enter into his judgment of whether or not a response has occurred. Rosenthal and Halas (1962) and Cordaro and Ison (1963) demonstrated the susceptibility of studies with *Planaria* to this sort of effect. While the studies of Corning and John (1961) and McConnell (1962) used blind procedures to circumvent this problem, much of the work in this area, including that on regeneration of planarians (v. supra) has ignored this problem instead of controlling for it.

If the inter-animal transfer effects obtained by McConnell's group are valid, they would seem to provide a tool of tremendous value for the study of chemical substrates of memory. There is, however, evidence to indicate that the effect is *not* a valid one. Hartry, Keith-Lee, and Morton (1964) replicated McConnell's procedures and elaborated upon them. These experimenters investigated the possibility that the results obtained in the earlier studies on inter-animal transfer effects in *Planaria* might be due to extraneous factors in the experimental situation such as sensitization to the CS, the UCS or other aspects of the situation such as the effects of feeding or handling. Hartry *et al*. ran two groups of planarians which were conditioned to criterion on a light-shock procedure. One of these became a trained donor group and the other a control which was tested for retention along with recipient groups. Three control groups were yoked to the trained donors. These received no training, but were given light, shock, or handling whenever the donors received these. Two additional control groups were run, one of which served as a recipient group for naïve donors, and the other as a naïve non-recipient control group. The experiment was run according to a blind procedure. It was found that any treatment of the donor planarians, whether handling, exposure to light or shock, or conditioning, resulted in faster learning of the conditioned response by the recipients. That is, all of these groups performed significantly better than did naïve planarians. In addition, the mere fact of ingestion of tissue appeared to have an effect, since all recipients of any donor animals learned more quickly than naïve animals, although not so quickly as the other groups mentioned. The rapid learning of the light-exposed, shock-exposed, and handled groups is similar to the performance of previously conditioned worms retrained after 24 hours. As Hartry *et al*. pointed out, their results do not exclude the possibility that memory transfer might exist, but they do provide a more plausible possible explanation for the results of studies of memory transfer in planarians. These results obtained by Hartry *et al*. have since been confirmed by Walker (Walker, 1966; Walker and Milton, 1966).

The work of Hartry *et al*. on sensitization effects in inter-animal transfer work with *Planaria* is part of a body of research which has indicated the possibility that all of the work on learning, intra-animal transfer, and inter-animal transfer in *Planaria* may be based largely on artifacts of the experimental situation. The major work in this area has been done by Halas and his associates. In their first study (Halas, James, and Stone, 1961) these experimenters investigated the possibility that light, which had been commonly used as a CS in *Planaria* conditioning, might be a UCS of sufficient potency to evoke behavior which appeared to be conditioning. They ran four groups of animals under the combination of light and shock pairing and found that light could elicit responses of cephalic turning and longitudinal body contraction. These responses occurred at high rates in animals exposed either to light or to shock, and did not occur in control animals which were not exposed to either. Furthermore, groups receiving paired light and shock did not differ from the groups receiving either alone. The authors concluded that while studies by the McConnell group

> used light as a CS, the results of the present study indicate that light is a US ... future investigators should be aware of the effects of strong light upon planaria (pp.304-5).

They note, however, that their study is not directly comparable to previous work because of procedural differences.

In a second study, Halas, James, and Knutson (1962) attempted to replicate the experiment of Thompson and McConnell (1955), which is generally cited as the reference experiment on classical conditioning of the planarian (*cf.* Kimble, 1961). The results obtained by Halas, James and Knutson showed marked differences from those of Thompson and McConnell. The differences, like the results of Halas, James, and Stone (1961), indicated that the light CS employed in the Thompson and McConnell procedure was actually acting as a US. The authors stated that

> the labeling of the phenomenon of pairing a weak US and a strong US as classical conditioning may not be correct ... perhaps it would be more accurate to use ... alpha conditioning or ... sensitization (reflex sensitization) as an explanation for the results (p. 971).

A further problem in work on classical conditioning of the planarian is pointed out by the experiment of Halas, Mulry, and DeBoer (1962) on the effects of polarity of the UCS shock electrodes. This study indicated clear behavioral differences in conditioning of a response involving approach to a light CS to escape shock as a function of polarity. This factor of differential sensitivity to current polarization was not, of course, controlled in earlier studies on planarian conditioning. It has particular relevance for the inter- and intra-animal transfer paradigms where variables such as this one and the unconditioned response to light shown by Halas, James, and Stone (1961) as well could easily lead to responses on the part of recipient animals which appear to be CRs, but are in fact the result of sensitization. The importance of sensitization as a confounding variable in inter-animal conditioning has already been pointed out by the work of Hartry *et al.* (1964).

In a later study James and Halas (1964a) attempted to determine whether conditioning occurred using the McConnell paradigm through the use of resistance to extinction as an index of learning. They felt that whereas measures during training might reflect the effects of such performance variables as sensitization, the demonstration of differences in resistance to extinction as a function of differing amounts of practice would provide a clear indication of learning. They trained 12 groups of planarians with 0, 150, 300, or 450 trials of either paired light and shock, light alone, or unpaired light and shock. Analyses of performance over 100 extinction trials indicated no differences among the 12 groups. James and Halas concluded that factors such as sensitization and pseudo-conditioning are the most likely explanation for the learning-like behavior observed in previous studies. In a reply to this paper, McConnell (1964) argued that the important factor in the previous work on planarian conditioning was not the exact nature of the learning but the fact that behavioral modifications were passed on after regeneration or ingestion, and so transfer of learning did occur. The question of conditioning *vs.* pseudo-conditioning *vs.* sensitization, he argued, is not the real issue.

The validity of McConnell's argument, as James and Halas (1964b) point out in their reply, is questionable. Transfer of learning cannot be demonstrated unless learning can be shown to have taken place in the donor animals. As was pointed out by the work of Hartry *et al.* (1964) and the studies of Halas and his co-workers just reviewed, sensitization of recipient animals might have led to a situation where responses occurred which appeared to be CRs but were in fact reflex responses to the CS.

A study was done recently by Jacobson, Horowitz, and Fried (1967) which attempted to demonstrate classical conditioning in the planarian while controlling for pseudo-conditioning and sensitization. In a series of experiments, these authors obtained evidence strongly suggestive of true conditioning. Thus, the question must remain open, at least for the time being.

In a recent symposium paper, Corning and Riccio (1967) reviewed in detail the entire planarian controversy. They reviewed 82 studies on learning in *Planaria,* ranging from habituation to instrumental conditioning, and found that 62 of these obtained positive results. They discussed the criticisms of Halas and his associates in detail, as well as other criticisms which have been published over the past several years. As might be expected, these authors concluded that planarians do show true conditioning. It should be noted, however, that this sort of scorekeeping does not tell the whole story. The major criticisms of the research with *Planaria* have been on grounds of methodology, and not solely of replicability. As they pointed out, many of the disputes have been semantic in nature, but many have been more fundamental than this. Work with planarians, therefore, has yielded results which provide only the most tentative evidence regarding chemical substrates of memory. While the results themselves appear encouraging and often spectacular, considerations such as experimenter bias, sensitization effects, and the question of whether planarians are actually conditionable limit the application of these results.

Research with Mammals

RNA Extraction Studies

Despite the fact that the evidence on inter-animal transfer of memory in *Planaria* was at best tenuous, it did stimulate interest in the possibility that a similar phenomenon might exist in higher animals. The first work on inter-animal transfer in rats was done by a group of Danish investigators (Fjerdingstad, Nissen, and Røigaard-Petersen, 1965) using a two-alley runway discrimination task for a water reward. Donor animals were trained on this task and then sacrificed. Their brains were removed and subjected to chemical procedures to extract their RNA. The extracted RNA was then injected intracisternally into naïve recipients, which were then tested on the same task. All donors and recipients were trained with light as the positive discrimination. Control groups received either RNA from naïve brains or no injection. Animals in the group receiving "trained" RNA were found to learn significantly more quickly than either of the controls, which did not differ.

In a second study (Nissen, Røigaard-Petersen and Fjerdingstad, 1965) the same experimenters investigated the effects of different types of training of donors on recipient behavior. In this study donors were trained on the same problem as was used in the earlier experiment, with the addition of a group trained on dark as the positive stimulus. Recipient animals were then trained either on the preference to which the donors had been conditioned or on the opposite preference until all were at approximately equal levels of performance, and then they were given reversal training. The results indicated an effect of the donor training that could be characterized as negative transfer. That is, animals injected with "light-trained" RNA performed better with dark as the positive stimulus, and vice versa. Nissen *et al.* reported no differences in running speed between any of their groups.

It should be noted that the purity of the RNA extracts used in these and other studies is open to question. As we shall discuss below, it is highly probable that they contained some amounts of protein and DNA, as well as phenol contamination from the extraction procedure.

Interest in memory transfer in this country began with a series of studies done by a group of investigators headed by Jacobson. In their first study (Babich, Jacobson, Bubash, and Jacobson, 1965) donor rats were trained to approach a food cup when a click was sounded. RNA extracted from the brains of these donors was injected intraperitoneally into naïve recipients which were then tested without reinforcement for approach to the food cup at the click signal. Control recipients were injected with RNA from naïve donors. Approach behavior was evaluated by two judges under a blind procedure. It was found that recipients of trained brain showed greater tendencies to approach the food cup than did controls. These results were extended to cross-species inter-animal transfer in a later study (Babich, Jacobson, and Bubash, 1965). In this experiment, a procedure identical to that of the first study was employed with the exception that the donor animals were hamsters and the recipients rats. Again, recipients of RNA from trained donors showed significantly greater approach behavior than did controls.

In another study (Jacobson, Babich, Bubash, and Jacobson, 1965) a differential procedure was employed. Two donor groups were trained to approach the food cup to either a click or a light. Recipients were tested with both stimuli, and showed a significant tendency to approach at the signal on which their donors were trained, and not on the other signal.

In a fourth study (Jacobson, Babich, Bubash, and Goren, 1966) Jacobson's group attempted to extend the memory transfer effect to include differential instrumental learning. For this purpose rats were trained in a double runway. An analysis of the number of rats which chose the "correct" side on a majority of trials as opposed to the number which did not indicated that there was a significant tendency for the recipients of "trained RNA" to follow their donors' preference. This, however, is an analysis of absolute preference. Any rat which went to the correct side 13 out of 25 trials or more was judged as having demonstrated transfer. Since a score of 13 out of 25 is very close to chance behavior in a two choice situation, it is instructive to examine the data Jacobson *et al.* present on the preferences of the individual rats. These data indicate that the vast majority of the rats chose the side to which their donors had been trained 15 out of 25 times or less. Only 4 rats out of 42 chose the correct side more than 16 times, and 13 chose this side 12 times or fewer. Thus, 25 rats out of 42 showed a weak (13 to 15 correct in 25 trials) tendency to respond according to their donors' preferences (*cf.* Barker, 1966, below).

The work of Jacobson's group has been subjected to extensive criticism. Carney (1965) criticized the first study (Babich *et al.*, 1965a) on several grounds. First he noted that while donor animals in this experiment were trained to eat from the food cup, the response measure used in the evaluation of recipient behavior was approach to the cup. Carney raised the question of whether any food cup-related behavior such as licking or chewing the cup had transferred. Second, Carney noted that control donors in the Babich *et al.* experiment were not subjected to any of the treatments given donors, *e. g.,* handling, feeding in the test box, exposure to clicks, food deprivation, etc. He noted the possibility that the Babich *et al.* results might have been due to some activating or alerting effect of the injections, and that failure to treat control donors might affect the activating factors. Third, Carney noted that the situation employed by Babich *et al.* might have been liable to pseudo-conditioning effects, and that it would have been desirable to test recipients for responsiveness to other stimuli as well as the critical one.

In his reply Jacobson (1965) noted that Carney's second and third criticisms were valid, and stated that other studies were being done to institute these controls—we have reviewed these studies (Jacobson *et al.*, 1965; 1966) above. With regard to Carney's first criticism, that of the response measure used, Jacobson's reply was that the actual consummatory response was only the end of a behavior chain involving approach. Carney's point, however, is an important one. It is possible that, through an activating effect on the injections, recipient animals in the Babich *et al.* experiment might have been merely orienting to the click; under certain conditions, this orientation could be scored as an approach response. Furthermore, if learning was being transferred, it would seem reasonable to expect some food cup activity on the part of the recipients. Babich *et al.* do not report this, nor does Jacobson in his reply to Carney.

Barker (1966) criticized the Jacobson *et al.* (1966) maze study. He stated, "All that a significantly large Chi square implies, in this case, is a lack of independence between 'preference of injected rats' and 'side to which donor was trained'. It does not indicate that one determined the other" (p. 314). In his reply, Jacobson (1966a) conceded that "perhaps in [the use of a 13 out of 25 criterion] we inadvertently capitalized on the vagaries of X^2 s" (p. 334). Jacobson further admitted that the conclusion of transfer of learning may have been "too strongly stated" (p.334).

In the Jacobson *et al.*(1966) maze study recipient animals, after being tested for preferences, were used as donors for the next replication. Worthington and Macmillan (1966) criticized this procedure, since it gave rise to a total of ten non-independent treatment groups rather than the one group assumed in the data analysis. Each of these ten groups differed in the nature of the material injected into its donors. Jacobson (1966b) replied to this that since all recipient-donors were trained to the same side as *their* donors, "any systematic biases in recipient animals are attributable to training of donor animals" (p. 298). This statement implied, in effect, that there will be no effect to the use of several "generations" of recipients. That is, it implies that injection of material from donor animals will have no effect upon the brains of the recipients. This is a questionable assumption at best. Indeed, if it were true, it would be difficult to conceive of how such injections would transfer learning.

It would appear, then, that the experiments of Jacobson's group do not provide unequivocal support for the phenomenon of memory transfer via "RNA extracts". It will be remembered, however, that the Danish experiments reviewed above (Fjerdingstad *et al.*, 1965; Nissen *et al.*, 1965) did indicate the possible existence of such an effect. Later experiments have continued to report negative results.

Corson and Enesco, in a series of unpublished studies, attempted to replicate the first Babich *et al.* (1965) study (John Corson, personal communication, 1966). These investigators performed several experiments, at first closely adhering to and later modifying the technique of Babich *et al.* Despite numerous behavioral and biochemical manipulations, they were never able to obtain transfer.

In their attempts to replicate the chemical manipulations of the Jacobson group, Corson and Enesco found that significant amounts of protein (peptide) material and of phenol (from the extraction procedures) were left in the so-called RNA extracts. In view of this and of Rosenblatt's work (below) it would be naïve to accept the Jacobson experiments at face value. Even if transfer were *clearly* shown in these studies (which it was not), the question of whether this was RNA-mediated, protein-mediated or complexly mediated transfer would remain. It is also important to note, in the light of the sensitization effects already discussed, that phenol might act as a stimulant.

Gross and Carey (1965) using apparatus and procedures virtually identical to those of Babich *et al.* also failed to find transfer.

Luttges, Johnson, Buck, Holland, and McGaugh (1966) performed a series of seven different experiments in which they attempted to obtain transfer using extracted RNA. The subjects in the seven experiments were variously rats and mice, and behavorial tasks included learning for both positive and negative reinforcement in maze, shuttle box, and passive avoidance situations. Extracted RNA was injected intraperitoneally in six of the experiments, and intraventricularly in the seventh. In an eighth experiment radioactively labelled extracts were injected to investigate the passage of intraperitoneally injected RNA extracts through the blood-brain barrier. None of the seven behavioral tests gave any evidence for learning transfer. Additionally, the labelling experiment indicated that the extracts were not getting into the brain. In view of their extensive attempts to obtain transfer and of the failure of Gross and Carey (1965) to replicate the findings of Babich *et al.*, Luttges *et al.* conclude "such negative findings suggest that the reported 'transfer' effect, if it exists, is either a very limited phenomenon or a very difficult one to reproduce" (p. 837).[3]

Halas, Bradfield, Sandlie, Theye, and Beardsley (1966) used a technique similar to that of Babich *et al.* (1965) with the addition of several control groups, including a non-injected group to provide data on base rates of responding in this situation. These investigators also failed to obtain RNA-mediated transfer.

Branch and Viney (1966) attempted to obtain transfer of a position discrimination. The use of a relatively simpler task such as this might be expected to favor the transfer effect, but these investigators, like the others, failed to obtain transfer.

In two papers, presented in 1966 and 1967, Essman reported results of a more positive nature using RNA extracts. Only abstracts of these papers are available at the time of this writing, and so it is difficult to assess the exact nature of the extracts used. In the first paper (Essman and Lehrer, 1966) rats were trained to escape a water maze, or were given motor training with no escape. It was found that RNA extracted from either the brains or the livers of donor rats was able to mediate transfer of learning as measured both by escape responses and by error reduction in the maze. No hypothesis is presented by Essman and Lehrer to explain the transfer via liver RNA.

In a second paper (Essman and Lehrer, 1967) a similar procedure was employed, this time in a water T-maze. Once again, RNA extracts from the brains of trained donors facilitated errorless performance as compared to those

[3] Copyright 1967, American Association for the Advancement of Science.

from untrained or motor trained donors. Essman and Lehrer further noted that recipients injected with yeast RNA did not differ from those injected with saline solution or with extracts from untrained or motor-trained donors. Although it is difficult to assess, the abstract indicates that a factorial design was used, and that recipients of extracts from like-trained donors were superior to those receiving extracts from opposite-trained donors, indicating the transfer of a specific response.

It is interesting to note that throughout the abstracts of their two reports, Essman and Lehrer place the terms "RNA" and "RNA extracts" in quotes. While no explanation is given for this, one might reasonably infer that this indicates a feeling on the part of the authors that the extracts contained material other than RNA. In the light of the studies reviewed alone, this does not seem improbable.

Gay and Raphelson (1967) extracted RNA from the brains of two groups of donor rats, one of which had received PAR training in a dark chamber. Despite the fact that rats normally will seek out a dark place, the recipients injected with RNA extracts from the PAR-trained groups showed significantly greater avoidance of the dark chamber. Similarly, Revusky and DeVenuto (1967) reported transfer of an aversion to saccharin solution via RNA extracts. This result is particularly interesting in view of the fact that the aversion was induced by X-irradiation. X-ray-induced aversion has been shown to transfer via blood factors from one member of a parabiotic preparation to the other (Hunt, Carroll, and Kimeldorf, 1965); this might indicate that some common factor is responsible for the transfer in the two situations.

At a recent and as yet unpublished symposium on this area of research, several papers were given which may shed light on this confused area. A full discussion of this work must await publication of the proceedings of this symposium. However, some mention of a few of these papers would seem appropriate at this time.

Rucker and Halstead (1967) reported a series of experiments in which they tested for the effects of injections of RNA extracted from yeast or from donor rats on discrimination learning of recipients. Yeast RNA was not found to affect behavior, a result consistent with those reviewed in Chapter V. Using the transfer paradigm, Rucker and Halstead found both positive and negative transfer effects. They suggested the existence of several "factors" in the extracts, each, so to speak, pulling in different directions. Evaluation of this notion must await publication of the full report.

In another paper at the symposium, McConnell, Shigehisa, and Salive (1967) presented data covering 2½ years of experiments in which over a thousand rats were tested for transfer via RNA. While their results were not unequivocal, there were strong indications that some sort of informational transfer can be made to occur, and that a start had been made toward delineating the mechanism for this transfer. Once again, full evaluation must await publication of the report.

As contradictory data continued to accumulate on the phenomenon of inter-animal transfer via RNA extracts, a report was published (Byrne *et al.*, 1966) summarizing the results obtained by 23 investigators at 7 different laboratories. All of these results questioned the reality of the phenomenon, because these experimenters had failed to obtain it using a variety of behavioral, chemical, and injection procedures. Byrne *et al.* emphasized two points. First, their negative findings do not necessarily indicate that this method of evaluating the possibility is not an adequate one. Second, their results bear only on memory transfer *via extracted RNA,* and it may be possible to obtain transfer by other means.

Non-RNA Studies

Ungar and Oceguera-Navarro (1965) investigated the possibility that the RNA extraction procedure might have a deleterious effect upon the brain factor mediating the transfer phenomenon. These investigators induced habituation of the startle response to sound in rats. When complete habituation had been obtained they sacrificed the animals, removed their brains, homogenized them and injected these whole brain homogenates into recipient mice. The mice were then tested for habituation to the same auditory stimulus. Control recipients received brain homogenates from untreated donors. Recipients of trained brain homogenates showed habituation to a 50% criterion in 1.25 days, as compared with 12.0 days in controls. Ungar and Oceguera-Navarro then treated trained brain homogenates with enzymes to investigate the nature of the chemical factor responsible for the transfer. They found that RNAse did not affect the transfer, while incubation with chymotrypsin, a protease, caused a loss of the transfer effect. They concluded that a "peptide-type material" (p. 302) was responsible for the transfer.

In a later study, Ungar (1966) investigated the specificity of this transfer of habituation. In these experiments, a design was employed wherein donor rats were habituated either to sound or air blast, and naïve recipients were tested for speed of habituation to both stimuli. Ungar found that the habituation transferred was specific to the donor training, a result suggesting that a simple depression of activity would not explain the earlier results.

Ungar extended these results to maze learning in two subsequent studies (Ungar, 1967; Ungar and Irwin, 1967). In these studies donors were trained on a left- or right-turn response in a Y maze, and recipients were tested for side preference, without reward. Again, response-specific transfer was obtained. Ungar concluded in these studies that while the mechanism for transfer is unclear, the medium seems to be proteins or peptides, and not nucleic acids.

Rosenblatt and his co-workers in an extensive series of experiments have explored various aspects of the inter-animal transfer effect. In their first paper (Rosenblatt, Farrow, and Herblin, 1966) they replicated the behavioral and extraction techniques of Babich *et al.* (1965) using RNA extracted from various portions of the brain as well as from the brain as a whole, the method used by

Babich *et al.* Additionally, two groups received RNA extract which had been incubated with RNAse to destroy their RNA. These extracts were from trained whole brain for one group and from trained cerebellum in the other. Aside from these added groups, the only major departure from the procedure of Babich *et al.* was in the use of pooled extracts—Babich *et al.* had injected each recipient rat with one donor's brain, while Rosenblatt *et al.* pooled all of the donor brains and divided the extract equally among recipients. The results of this study indicated a significant transfer effect, although somewhat weaker than that obtained by Babich *et al.* with the same training and extraction procedures. Furthermore, the cerebellar extracts and the RNA-free extracts proved to be as potent as the cerebral extract. Through further testing Rosenblatt *et al.* demonstrated that the extracts used by Jacobson's group probably contained significant amounts of protein, contrary to the reported absence of protein by Babich *et al.* (1965).

In a second paper Rosenblatt, Farrow, and Rhine (1966) performed a series of ten experiments to investigate certain parameters of the inter-animal transfer phenomenon. These included possible activity differences between recipients of trained and untrained extracts, the range and specificity of behavior which is transferrable, the chemical nature of the transfer substance, and the effects of various behavioral manipulations. A variety of tasks was used, including the click-approach paradigm of Babich *et al,* active and passive avoidance, and simple Skinner box and Y-maze spatial discriminations. All of these tasks were found to be susceptible to transfer. Some indication was found that tasks which make use of a definite cue stimulus such as a click or a light transfer more readily than tasks without these cues.

Activity measures showed a significant effect in this study. Recipients of trained brain extracts were more active than controls in terms of their respective bar press rates. Rosenblatt *et al.* also compared the pooled brain extract method used in their previous study with the 1:1 method of Babich *et al.* No significant difference was found between these techniques.

In their consideration of the various types of extracts used, Rosenblatt, Farrow, and Rhine noted several points of interest. First, while both cerebral and cerebellar extracts were shown to support transfer, the cerebellar extracts were considerably less potent. Second, the finding of Rosenblatt, Farrow, and Rhine (1966) and of Ungar and Oceguara-Navarro (1965) that incubation with RNAse did not affect transfer was confirmed. Third, it was noted that the extract of greatest potency was the tissue fraction with a molecular weight range from 1,000 to 5,000, although transfer effects were found for molecular weight fractions up to 10,000. The fact that no fractions over 10,000 were effective as transfer media indicates that large proteins are probably not involved in transfer. Rosenblatt *et al.* concluded that the transfer molecule is most probably a polypeptide.

Rosenblatt and Miller (1966) investigated the dose-response relationships involved in the transfer phenomenon using spatial discrimination training as the behavioral test. They found that at low doses (equivalent to one donor brain per recipient or less) there is often negative transfer. That is, the recipients respond opposite to the donors' training. Rosenblatt and Miller refer to this phenomenon as an "inversion effect", and state that it might be due to the transfer at low doses of a general familiarity with the situation without transfer of specific learned responses. This familiarity would reduce fear and cause the rats to show more exploratory behavior in the apparatus, and therefore poorer performance on the learning task. With increasing doses, more specific behaviors are transferred, resulting in better performance.

They stated that failures to obtain transfer such as those reported by Byrne et al. (1966) may be due to behavioral ambiguities caused by inversion to transfer. They further noted that the use of RNA extracts might be detrimental to obtaining transfer, since their results indicate that RNA is not involved.

Albert (1966) approached the problem of memory transfer in a way which is very different from the studies we have reviewed thus far. His procedure consisted of training rats on an avoidance task, confining learning to one hemisphere by cortical spreading depression (CSD). He found that removal of the medial cortex of the trained hemisphere impaired retention of the learning, but intra-peritoneal injection of the extirpated tissue back into the donor animal caused savings in relearning by the trained hemisphere. This injection effect was found to be specific to the previously learned response, and proved to be localized in the nuclei of the cells of the extirpated cortex. Further tests indicated a macromolecular nuclear substance, so Albert incubated the nuclear fractions with either RNAse or the protease trypsin. The savings was affected adversely by RNAse, but unaffected by trypsin, leading Albert to conclude that the critical factor was RNA.

The results obtained by Albert appear both striking and significant, as indeed they may be. However, one important control is lacking, without which the significance of Albert's effect cannot be assessed. Specifically, it is necessary to inject the homologous cortical tissue from a naïve donor into a trained recipient in order to know for certain that an "engram" is being replaced. Failure to do this leaves open the possibility that injection of brain tissue might have some non-specific effect.[4] A further desirable control would be the injection of RNA, whether from yeast or extracted from some other "neutral" source to investigate possible sensitization effects.

Further supportive evidence for the existence of inter-animal transfer has come from two studies by Byrne and his collaborators, both available only as abstracts at this time. In the first of these (Byrne and Samuel, 1966), it was found that the bar-pressing response in a Skinner box situation was susceptible to transfer. In the second (Byrne and Hughes, 1967) this result was extended to include transfer of a spatial (two bar) Skinner box discrimination. Byrne and Hughes expressed the belief that synaptic modification via new protein synthesis

[4] I am grateful to J. F. Lubar for pointing this out.

was the basis for information storage. Evaluation of this work must await the publication of a full report.

Dyal, Golub and Marrone (1967) confirmed and extended the findings of Byrne's group on transfer of the bar-press response. These investigators tested both for transfer of bar pressing and for approaches to the feeding mechanisms (measured by crossing of a photocell beam). They ran two experimental groups, each with yoked controls. The first received only continuous reinforcement training, while the second received this and also extinction and reacquisition training. They found (and replicated) transfer both of bar pressing and of magazine approach only in the second, more extensively trained group. Dyal, *et al.* advanced the hypothesis that some general activating factor might be involved in the transfer effect, since in their laboratory transfer and heightened activity seem to occur together.

Another study by this group (Dyal and Golub, 1967a) studied transfer of a black-white (brightness) discrimination, and found that while some transfer may have occurred, application of a particularly rigorous statistical procedure indicated that it had not. Specifically, in this experiment donor rats were trained to approach either a black or a white alley, and this preference was to be transferred to donors via injections of brain homogenates. Recipient rats were assigned their injections on the basis of their pre-injection preference for black or white, recipients being given injections which went *against* their initial preference. In their analysis of change scores (number of post-injection choices of the "correct" side minus number of pre-injection choices), Dyal and Golub reported that 12 Ss showed positive scores (preferred the "correct" stimulus), three showed negative scores (preferred their original stimulus), and three showed scores of 0 (showed no preference). As Dyal and Golub noted, this type of data is generally analyzed by use of the sign test, which ignores tied scores (scores of 0). Analysis by this method indicates a significant shift of the Ss' preferences. However, if the three Ss with scores of zero are considered to have gone *against* the hypothesis, *i.e.* are grouped with those Ss showing negative scores, the results fail to support the transfer hypothesis. As the authors point out, in an area such as this one it behooves researchers to report all results, positive *and* negative, and to take the most conservative statistical approach. The two possible interpretations of these data illustrate this point well.

In a later paper at the AAAS symposium, Dyal and Golub (1967b) investigated the question raised by their first experiment of the specificity of the transfer effect. Again, a full report of this paper is not yet available, but after reviewing the work done in their laboratory, the authors concluded that the transfer effect they obtained was, indeed, a real phenomenon which could not be accounted for by a simple activation or sensitization model, although some non-specific activation effect might have been involved.

In another study reported at the AAAS symposium, Krech, Bennett, and Ragan (1967) utilized a novel technique for a study of the transfer effect. These experimenters sought to optimize conditions for the transfer effect to take place by providing an already-organized memory system for the injected material to reactivate. They used a procedure developed by Campbell and Jaynes (1966) called "memory reinstatement." In this procedure groups of weanling rats (about 21 days old) are exposed to inescapable foot shock in a black box, with rest periods in a white box. When tested four weeks later, none of these rats showed any retention for the experience (*i.e.*, they showed no aversion to the black box or preference for the white). Another group, however, which received the same treatment at 21 days, and in addition were given one-minute "refresher courses" once each week during the four-week retention period, showed excellent retention and preferred the white box. (A third group received only the "refresher course," and after four weeks showed no preference for the white box.) Krech *et al.* emphasized that this experience is retained only if the nervous system is given occasional "reminders," and attempted to substitute injections of brain homogenates from trained animals for the weekly "refresher courses." Their data were not wholly unequivocal, but in a series of experiments using several different procedures, they found that injections of trained brain homogenates, and occasionally also liver homogenates, served as effective memory boosters. The results with liver are not readily understandable, but it is noteworthy that Essman and Lehrer (1966, above) reported a similar result. Evaluation of these data must await publication of the complete report, but assuming that this is a replicable effect, this may provide a task which could be used to study the transfer phenomenon, as is clear from this review. Much time has been spent so far in attempting to determine the conditions under which transfer occurs reliably so that the phenomenon itself can then be studied. This task, if it is replicable, is simple and straightforward enough to provide the medium whereby experimenters can go on to investigate the more basic aspects of the phenomenon.

Many of the studies of inter-animal transfer reviewed thus far have yielded equivocal results for a number of reasons. First, there is often the possibility that transfer effects, when they are obtained, might be accounted for by sensitization effects or effects of the injected substances on activity. Second, the studies in this area have often been contaminated by the use of unnecessary complications which might affect their results. These include cross-species transfer, poor chemical technique, and extraction of specific substances such as RNA for injection. Third, the behavioral tasks employed have not generally been exploited to the fullest extent possible. For example, in a discrimination task it would be desirable to use visual rather than spatial discrimination because the former is less subject to motor effects. It would also be desirable to investigate the possibility of obtaining negative as well as positive transfer effects on the discrimination task, in view of the fact that both types of results have been reported (Nissen *et al.*, 1965; Rosenblatt and Miller, 1966; Rucker and Halstead, 1967). Further, the use of a factorial design might serve to facilitate observation of the effects of the inversion phenomenon noted by Rosenblatt and Miller (1966), since this would show up as a facilitatory effect in negative transfer groups.

Gurowitz (1967) attempted to meet these needs and, in addition, to increase the probability of obtaining transfer by pre-training his donors. Also, he attempted to control for contaminating factors such as activation or sensitization. He used whole brain dialysates to provide for a minimum possibility of chemical error and at the same time allow for transfer via a variety of possible chemical media. Furthermore, use of a visual discrimination task, multiple measures of learning and performance, and non-injected control groups, as well as those injected with naïve brain, provided additional controls.

In this study, Gurowitz failed to find any indication of transfer, either positive or negative, as measured by trials to criterion or by progress of learning. He also failed to find any systematic effect on response rates. In a further investigation of the transfer phenomenon, Gurowitz and Gross (1968) measured changes in overall activity level (Ss were housed in running wheels with cages attached for 18 days), food intake and water intake as a function of injections of brain material. They found that injections of any brain homogenates, whether from trained or naïve donors, caused a transitory decrease in activity (one day) and in food intake (two days). Gurowitz and Gross attributed this depression of function to illness in the rats caused by immune reactions to the homogenates, and suggested that the existence of this depression might account for the positive results of earlier transfer studies, which tested animals during the depressed period. In the study of Ungar and Oceguera-Navarro (1966), for example, animals tested during the depressed period might have appeared to show rapid habituation, because habituation is facilitated by depressed agents. This hypothesis is complicated, however, by Ungar's later finding (1966) that the transfer was of a more specific nature than would be expected from this view.

Summary of Inter-animal Transfer

The research we have reviewed in this chapter is far from clear in its implications. From an *a priori* standpoint, the evidence that memory is chemical in nature makes the idea of inter-animal transfer seem plausible. The early planarian work seemed to indicate that such a phenomenon did exist, but later research indicated that certain very basic problems complicated this view. First of all, there is the question of whether planarians are capable of showing true learning. Despite a great deal of research and debate, this question remains unresolved. Secondly, evidence exists to indicate that the planarian inter-animal transfer results might be attributable to sensitization effects.

Similarly, the early work with mammalian species seemed to indicate transfer, both via RNA and other media. Here, as in the planarian work, negative evidence was quick to accumulate. More recently, the pendulum seems to be swinging back as a number of researchers report positive results. A major problem in this area has been and continues to be the difficulty involved in comparing the work of various laboratories. What appear to be superficially similar methods of procedure when they are written up in the literature often differ in subtle ways which render the studies incomparable. These differences are often semantic in nature—what one investigator calls "brain homogenate" or "RNA extract" often differs greatly from a substance given a similar label by another investigator. The most pressing need in this area at present is for a standardization of techniques and terminology so that researchers can work toward delineating the mechanisms involved in transfer. It is important to remember that while the transfer phenomenon is interesting in itself, it is most important in its role as a tool for the investigation of the larger problem of the nature of the chemical basis for memory. This goal must be kept in view.

Another important point should be kept in mind in reviewing this area. The notion of a chemical basis for memory makes the idea of inter-animal transfer plausible. If such transfer exists, then we have strong evidence in support of the chemical view. If, however, there is no such phenomenon, this does not provide evidence *against* the chemical view, but indicates only that whatever chemical changes take place in memory are specific to the particular animal doing the learning.

In general, however, the data seem to indicate that the inter-animal transfer phenomenon is a real, albeit highly elusive, effect, probably based on a polypeptide or small protein medium.

chapter
VIII

CONCLUSION

In surveying the literature in this complex area, the only fact which becomes clear is the lack of clarity. The view that memory, or at least long-term memory, is chemical in its basis seems well established, and furthermore, it seems certain that this memory substrate must be macro-molecular in nature. The identity of the memory molecule (if indeed, it is a single molecule) is, however, unknown.

The major candidates for roles in memory, as we have seen, are the nucleic acids and protein. DNA, an attractive choice because of its role in the encoding and storage of genetic information, seems on closer inspection to be an unlikely candidate because of its extreme stability with respect to environmental influences. RNA has been considered extensively, and cannot be wholly disregarded at this time despite a large amount of negative evidence. The evidence on protein also seem favorable, especially evidence obtained from experiments using drugs which affect protein metabolism.

The data we have reviewed do not allow us to reject unequivocally any of the potential candidates for a role in memory. Even DNA may have some role, as we have discussed, in terms of gene activation. Theorizing in this area has begun to move from the rather naïve and simplistic one-molecule view toward theories based on the more sophisticated ideas of molecular biology, especially toward the DNA-RNA-protein complex view involved in the new gene activation (or DNA derepression) theories.

On the whole, considering our present state of knowledge (or ignorance) in this area, little can be said with certainty about the nature of the memory molecule. Indeed, in the face of some of the negative evidence we have reviewed, to hold to a strictly molecular view of memory requires something of an act of faith. Most probably, the extreme or strict molecular view, like most extreme views, is not adequate by itself, as we have discussed. In my opinion, research in the next few years will bring us to a position where the "molar" and "molecular" views of learning and memory discussed in Chapter II will come to complement each other, and the research we have reviewed in this volume will lead to an elucidation of the first step in a chain of events which has as its end result the neural encoding and readout of memory.

At the present time, however, it is safe to say, that we still know relatively little about the molecular basis of memory. Our present ignorance in this area, however, is far less than the ignorance of ten years ago. We can, therefore, reasonably hope that it will be still less ten years hence.

REFERENCES

Albert, D. J., "Memory in mammals: evidence for a system involving nuclear ribonucleic acid," *Neuropsychologia,* 4 (1966), 79-93.

Andjus, R. K., F. Knopfelmacher, R. W. Russel, and A. U. Smith, "Some effects of severe hypothermia on learning and retention," *Quart. J. exp. Psychol.,* 8 (1956), 15-23.

Babich, F. R., A. L. Jacobson, and S. Bubash, "Cross-species transfer of learning: effect of ribonucleic acid from hamsters on rat behavior," *Proc. Nat. Acad. Sci. (USA),* 54 (1965), 1299-1302.

Babich, F. R., A. L. Jacobson, S. Bubash, and A. Jacobson, "Transfer of a response to naïve rats by injection of ribonucleic acid extracted from trained rats," *Science,* 144 (1965), 656-57.

Barker, D. J., "Comment on Jacobson *et al.,*" *Psychon. Sci.,* 4 (1966), 314.

Barondes, S. H., and S. D. Cohen, "Puromycin effect on successive phases of memory storage," *Science,* 151 (1966), 594-95.

———, "Comparative effects of cycloheximide and puromycin on cerebral protein synthesis and consolidation of memory in mice," *Brain Res.,* 4 (1967a), 44-51.

———, "Delayed and sustained effect of acetoxycycloheximide on memory in mice," *Proc. Nat. Acad. Sci. (USA),* 59 (1967b), 157-64.

Barondes, S. H., and M. E. Jarvik, "Influence of actinomycin-D on brain RNA synthesis and memory," *J. Neurochem.,* 11 (1964), 187.

Batkin, S., W. T. Woodward, R. E. Cole, and J. B. Hall, "RNA and actinomycin-D enhancement of learning in the carp," *Psychon. Sci.,* 5 (1966). 345-46.

Bowman, R., "Magnesium pemoline and behavior," *Science,* 153 (1966), 902.

Branch, J. C., and W. Viney, "An attempt to transfer a position discrimination habit via RNA extracts," *Psychol. Rep.,* 19 (1966) 923-26.

Briggs, M. H., and G. B. Kitto, "The molecular basis of memory and learning," *Psychol. Rev.,* 69 (1962), 537-41.

Brodsky, V. Ya., "Effect of barbamil and of urethane on the nucleic acids of the spinal cord," *Dokl. Akad. Nauk SSSR,* 112 (1957), 753-55.

Brown, H., "Effect of ribonucleic acid (RNA) on the rate of lever pressing in rats," *Psychol. Rec.,* 16 (1966), 173-76.

Brush, T. R., J. W. Davenport, and V. J. Polidora, "TCAP: negative results in avoidance and water maze learning and retention," *Psychon. Sci.,* 4 (1966), 183-84.

Bureš, J., and O. Burešová, "Cortical spreading depression as a memory disturbing factor," *J. comp. physiol. Psychol.,* 56 (1963) 268-73.

Byrne, W. L., and A. Hughes, "Behavioral modification by injection of brain extract from trained donors," *Fed. Proc.,* 26 (1967), 676 (Abstract).

Byrne, W. L., and D. Samuel, "Behavioral modification by injection of brain extract prepared from a trained donor," *Science,* 154 (1966), 418 (Abstract).

Byrne, W. L., and 22 others, "Memory transfer," *Science,* 153 (1966), 658.

Caldwell, D. F., and J. A. Churchill, "Learning ability in the progeny of rats administered a protein-deficient diet during the second half of gestation," *Neurology,* 17 (1967), 95-99.

Cameron, D. E., "The use of nucleic acid in aged patients with memory impairment," *Amer. J. Psychiat.,* 114 (1958), 943.

——, "The processes of remembering," *Brit. J. Psychiat.,* 109 (1963), 325-40.

Cameron, D. E., and L. Solyom, "Effects of ribonucleic acid on memory," *Geriatrics,* 16 (1961), 74-81.

Cameron, D. E., L. Solyom, S. Sved, and B. Wainrib, "Effects of intravenous administration of ribonucleic acid upon failure of memory for recent events in presenile and aged individuals," *Rec. Adv. Biol. Psychiat.,* 5 (1962), 365-74.

Cameron, D. E., S. Sved, L. Solyom, B. Wainrib, and H. Barik, "Effects of ribonucleic acid on memory defect in the aged," *Amer. J. Psychiat.,* 120 (1963), 320-25.

Campbell, B., and J. Jaynes, "Reinstatement," *Psychol. Rev.,* 73 (1966), 478-80.

Carney, R. E., "Transfer of learned response by RNA injection," *Science,* 150 (1965), 228.

Chamberlain, T. J., G. H. Rothschild, and R. W. Gerard, "Drugs affecting RNA and learning," *Proc. Nat. Acad. Sci. (USA),* 49 (1963), 918-24.

Chitre, V. S., S. P. Chopra, and G. P. Talwar, "Changes in the ribonucleic acid content of the brain during experimentally induced convulsions," *J. Neurochem.,* 11 (1964), 439.

Chorover, S. L., and P. H. Schiller, "Short-term retrograde amnesia in rats," *J. comp. physiol. Psychol.,* 59 (1965). 73-78.

———, "Reexamination of prolonged retrograde amnesia in one-trial learning," *J. comp. physiol. Psychol.*, 61 (1966), 31-41.

Cohen, H. D., and S. H. Barondes, "Further studies of learning and memory after intracerebral actinomycin-D," *J. Neurochem.*, 13 (1966a), 207-11.

———, "Lack of effect of a highly purified yeast RNA preparation on maze learning," *Psychopharmacologia*, 8 (1966b), 375-79.

Cohen, H. D., F. Ervin, and S. H. Barondes, "Puromycin and cycloheximide: different effects on hippocampal electrical activity," *Science*, 154 (1966), 1557-58.

Cook, L., A. B. Davidson, D. J. Davis, H. Green, and E. J. Fellows, "Ribonucleic acid: effect on conditioned behavior in rats," *Science*, 141 (1963), 268-69.

Coons, E. E., and N. E. Miller, "Conflict versus consolidation of memory traces to explain 'retrograde amnesia' produced by ECS," *J. comp. physiol. Psychol.*, 53 (1960), 524-31.

Cordaro, L., and J. R. Ison, "Psychology of the scientist: observer bias in classical conditioning of the planarian," *Psychol. Rep.*, 13 (1963), 787-89.

Corning, W. C., and E. R. John, "Effect of ribonuclease on retention of conditioned response in regenerated planarians," *Science*, 34 (1961), 1363-65.

Corning, W. C., and D. J. Riccio, "The planarian controversy." Paper presented at AAAS symposium on Molecular Approaches to Learning and Memory, December, 1967.

Corson, J. A., and H. E. Enesco, "Some effects of injections of ribonucleic acid," *Psychon. Sci.*, 5 (1966), 217-18.

Crick, F. H. C., "Structure of the hereditary material," *Scient. Amer.*, 191 (1954), 54-61.

Cyert, L. A., K. E. Moyer, and J. A. Chapman, "Effect of magnesium pemoline on learning and memory of a one-way avoidance response," *Psychon. Sci.*, 7 (1967), 9-10.

Davidson, A. B., L. Cook, and D. J. Davis, "RNA tetranucleotides in avoidance acquisition: replication and limitations on interpretation of results." Paper presented at Eastern Psychological Association Meetings, Boston, April, 1967.

Davis, R. E., and B. W. Agranoff, "Stages of memory formation in goldfish: evidence for an environmental trigger." *Proc. Nat. Acad. Sci. (USA)*, 55 (1966), 555-59.

Deutsch, J. A., and D. Deutsch, *Physiological Psychology*. Homewood, Ill.: Dorsey, 1966.

Dingman, W., and M. B. Sporn, "The incorporation of 8-azaguanine into rat brain RNA and its effect on maze learning by the rat: an inquiry into the biochemical basis of memory," *J. psychiat. Res.*, 1 (1961), 1-11.

———, "Molecular theories of memory," *Science*, 144 (1964), 26-29.

Duncan, C. P., "Habit reversal induced by electroshock in the rat," *J. comp. physiol. Psychol.*, 41 (1948), 11-16.

Dureman, E. I., "Differential patterning of behavioral effects from three types of stimulant drugs," *Clin. Pharmacol. & Therap.,* 3 (1962), 29-33.

Dyal, J. A., and A. M. Golub, "An attempt to obtain shifts in brightness preference as a function of injection of brain homogenate," *J. biol. Psychol.,* 9 (1967a), 29-33.

——, "Behavioral transfer via injection of brain homogenate: activation or specificity?" Paper presented to AAAS symposium on Molecular Approaches to Learning and Memory, December, 1967.

Dyal, J. A., A. M. Golub, and R. L. Marrone, "Transfer effects of intraperitoneal injection of brain homogenates," *Nature,* 214 (1967), 720-21.

Eberts, F. S., Jr., "1,1,3-Tricyano-2-amino-1-propene (U-9189), a biologically-active component of aqueous solutions of malononitrile," *Biochem. Biophys. Res. Comm.,* 3 (1960), 107-9.

Egyházi, E., and H. Hydén, "Experimentally induced changes in the base composition of the ribonucleic acids of isolated nerve cells and their oligodendroglial cells." *J. Biophys. Biochem. Cytol.,* 10 (1961), 403-10.

Eist, H., and U.S. Seal, "The permeability of the blood-brain barrier and blood-CSF barrier to C^{14} tagged ribonucleic acid," *Amer. J. Psychiat.,* 122 (1965), 584-86.

Essman, W. B., "Effect of tricyanoaminopropene on the amnesic effect of electroconvulsive shock," *Psychopharmacologia,* 9 (1966), 426-33.

Essman, W. B., and G. M. Lehrer, "Is there a chemical transfer of training?" *Fed. Proc.,* 25 (1966), 208 (Abstract).

——, "Facilitation of maze performances by 'RNA extracts' from maze-trained mice," *Fed. Proc.,* 26 (1967), 263 (Abstract).

Falbe-Hansen, J., and H. Pakkenberg, "Nerve cells of the vestibular and spiral ganglia in guinea pigs following arsacetin poisoning," *Dan. med. Bull.,* 10 (1963), 207-9.

Fjerdingstad, E. J., Th. Nissen, and H. H. Røigaard-Petersen, "Effect of ribonucleic acid (RNA) extracted from the brain of trained animals on learning in rats," *Scand. J. Psychol.,* 6 (1965), 1-6.

Flexner, J. B., L. B. Flexner, and E. Stellar, "Memory in mice as affected by intracerebral puromycin," *Science,* 141 (1963), 57-59.

Flexner, J. B., L. B. Flexner, E. Stellar, G. De La Haba, and R. B. Roberts, "Inhibition of protein synthesis in brain and learning and memory following puromycin," *J. Neurochem.,* 9 (1962), 595-605.

Flexner, L. B., "Loss of memory in mice as related to regional inhibition of cerebral protein synthesis," *Tex. Rep. Biol. Med.,* 24 (1966), 3-19.

Flexner, L. B., J. B. Flexner, and R. B. Roberts, "Stages of memory in mice treated with acetoxycycloheximide before or immediately after learning," *Proc. Nat. Acad. Sci. (USA), 56 (1966), 730-35.*

——, "Memory in mice analyzed with antibiotics," *Science,* 155 (1967),1377-83.

Fruton, J. S., and S. Simmonds, *General Biochemistry* (2nd ed.). New York: John Wiley & Sons, Inc., 1958.

Gaito, J., "A biochemical approach to learning and memory," *Psychol. Rev.,* 68 (1961), 288-92.

——, "DNA and RNA as memory molecules," *Psychol. Rev.*, 70 (1963), 471-80.

——, "Nucleic acids and brain function," in *Symposium on the Role of Macromolecules in Complex Behavior.* 1964, Kansas State University (unpublished).

——, *Molecular Psychobiology.* Springfield, Ill.: Charles C Thomas, Publisher, 1966.

Gaito, J., and A. Zavala, "Neurochemistry and learning," *Psychol. Bull.*, 61 (1964), 45-62.

Gay, R., and A. Raphelson, " 'Transfer of learning' by injection of brain RNA: a replication," *Psychon. Sci.*, 8 (1967), 369-70.

Gerard, R. W., "Material basis of memory," *J. vbl. Lng. vbl. Behav.*, 2 (1963), 22-33.

——, "What is memory?" *Scient. Amer.*, 189 (1953), 118-26.

Glasky, A. J., and L. N. Simon, "Magnesium pemoline: enhancement of brain RNA polymerases," *Science*, 151 (1966), 702-3.

Goldberg, I. H., M. Rabinowitz, and E. Reich, "Basis of actinomycin action. I: DNA binding and inhibition of RNA polymerase-synthetic reactions by actinomycin," *Proc. Nat. Acad. Sci. (USA)*, 48 (1962), 2094-2101.

——, "Basis of actinomycin action. II: Effect of actinomycin on the nucleoside triphosphate-inorganic pyrophosphate reaction," *Proc. Nat. Acad. Sci. (USA)*, 49 (1963), 226-28.

Goldsmith, L. J., "Effect of intracerebral actinomycin-D and of electroconvulsive shock on passive avoidance," *J. comp. physiol. Psychol.*, 63 (1967), 126-32.

Gross, C., and F. M. Carey, "Transfer of learned response by RNA injection: failure of attempts to replicate," *Science*, 150 (1965), 1749.

Grossman, S. P., *Textbook of Physiological Psychology.* New York: John Wiley & Sons, Inc., 1967.

Gurowitz, E. M., "An investigation of inter-animal transfer of learning via brain homogenates," Unpublished doctoral dissertation, University of Rochester, 1967.

Gurowitz, E. M., and D. A. Gross, "Effects of injections of brain homogenates on activity and on food and water intake." Paper presented at Eastern Psychological Association meetings, Washington, D. C., April, 1968.

Gurowitz, E. M., D. A. Gross, and R. George, "Effects of TCAP on passive avoidance learning in the rat." Paper in preparation.

Gurowitz, E. M., and J. F. Lubar, "Changes in activity, food ingestion, and passive avoidance behavior following limbic-septal ablation in the cat," *Proc. 74th Annu. Conv. Amer. Psychol. Assoc.*, 2 (1966), 107-8.

Gurowitz, E. M., J. F. Lubar, B. R. Ain, and D. A. Gross, "Disruption of passive avoidance learning by magnesium pemoline," *Psychon. Sci.*, 8 (1967), 19-20.

Halas, E. S., K. Bradfield, M. E. Sandlie, F. Theye, and J. Beardsley, "Changes in rat behavior due to RNA injection," *Physiol. & Behav.*, 1 (1966), 281-83.

Halas, E. S., R. L. James, and C. S. Knutson, "An attempt at classical conditioning in the planarian," *J. comp. physiol. Psychol.*, 55 (1962), 969-71.

Halas, E. S., R. L. James, and L. A. Stone, "Types of responses elicited in planaria by light," *J. comp. physiol. Psychol.*, 54 (1961), 302-5.

Halas, E. S., R. C. Mulry, and M. De Boer, "Some problems involved in conditioning planaria: electrical polarity," *Psychol. Rep.*, 11 (1962), 395-98.

Hamberger, C.-A., and H. Hydén, "Cytochemical changes in the cochlear ganglion caused by acoustic stimulation and trauma," *Acta Otolaryng.* (1945), Supp. 61.

——, "Transneuronal chemical changes in Deiter's nucleus," *Acta Otolaryng.* (1949), Supp. 75, 82-113.

Hartry, A. L., P. Keith-Lee, and W. D. Morton, "Planaria: memory transfer through cannibalism reexamined," *Science,* 146 (1964), 274-75.

Hebb, D. O., *The Organization of Behavior.* New York: John Wiley & Sons, Inc., 1949.

Hebb, D. O., and K. Williams, "A method of rating animal intelligence," *J. genet. Psychol.*, 34 (1946), 59-65.

Hunt, E. L., H. W. Carroll, and D. S. Kimeldorf, "Humoral mediation of radiation-induced motivation in parabiont rats," *Science,* 150 (1965) 1747-48.

Hurwitz, J., T. T. Furth, M. Malamy, and M. Alexander, "The role of deoxyribonucleic acid in ribonucleic acid synthesis, III. The inhibition of the enzymatic synthesis of RNA and DNA by actinomycin-D and proflavin," *Proc. Nat. Acad. Sci. (USA),* 48 (1962), 1222-30.

Hydén, H., "Behavior, neural function and RNA," *Progr. in nucl. Acid Res.,* 6 (1967), 187-218.

——, "Protein metabolism in the nerve cell during growth and function," *Acta Physiol. Scand.,* 6 (1943), Supp. 17.

——, "The neuron," in *The Cell,* J. Brachet and A. E. Mirsky, Vol. 4. 1960. New York: Academic Press, Inc., 1960. Pp. 215-323.

——, "The neuron and its glia—a biochemical and functional unit," *Endeavour,* 21 (1962), 144-55.

Hydén, H., and E. Egyházi, "Nuclear RNA changes of nerve cells during a learning experiment in rats," *Proc. Nat. Acad. Sci. (USA),* 48 (1962), 1366-73.

——, "Glial RNA changes during a learning experiment with rats," *Proc. Nat. Acad. Sci. (USA),* 49 (1963), 618-24.

——, "Changes in RNA and base composition in cortical neurons of rats in a learning experiment involving transfer of handedness," *Proc. Nat. Acad. Sci. (USA),* 52 (1964), 1030-35.

Hydén, H., and H. Hartelius, "Stimulation of the nucleo-protein production in the nerve cells by malononitrile and its effect on psychic functions in mental disorders," *Acta Psychiat. Neurol.* (1948), Supp. 48.

Hydén, H., and P. W. Lange, "Differentiation in RNA response in neurons early and late in learning," *Proc. Nat. Acad. Sci. (USA),* 53 (1965), 946-52.

Hydén, H., and A. Pigon, "Cytophysical study of the functional relationship between oligodendroglial cells and nerve cells of Deiter's nucleus," *J. Neurochem.*, 6 (1960), 57-72.

Ison, J. R., and P. Taplin, "Reagent grade yeast RNA injections and rat performance in the Hebb-Williams maze," *Psychon. Sci.*, 6 (1966), 495-96.

Jacobson, A. L., "Reply to Carney," *Science*, 150 (1965), 228.

——, "Reply to Barker," *Psychon, Sci.*, 4 (1966a), 334.

——, "Reply to Worthington and Macmillan," *Psychon. Sci.*, 5 (1966b), 298.

Jacobson, A. L., F. R. Babich, S. Bubash, and C. Goren, "Maze preferences in naïve rats produced by injection of ribonucleic acid from trained rats," *Psychon. Sci.*, 4 (1966), 3-4.

Jacobson, A. L., F. R. Babich, S. Bubash, and A. Jacobson, "Differential approach tendencies produced by injection of ribonucleic acid from trained rats," *Science*, 150 (1965), 636-37.

Jacobson, A. L., S. D. Horowitz, and C. Fried, "Classical conditioning, pseudo-conditioning, or sensitization in the planarian," *J. comp. physiol. Psychol.*, 64 (1967), 73-79.

James, R. L., and E. S. Halas, "No difference in extinction behavior in planaria following various types and amounts of training," *Psychol. Rec.*, 14 (1964a), 1-11.

——, "A reply to McConnell," *Psychol. Rec.*, 14 (1964b), 21-23.

Jones, J. E., "Contiguity and reinforcement in relation to CS-UCS intervals in classical aversive conditioning," *Psychol. Rev.*, 69 (1962), 176-86.

Karlson, P., *Introduction to Modern Biochemistry*. New York: Academic Press, Inc., 1963.

Katz, J. J., and W. C. Halstead, "Protein organization and mental function," *Comp. Psychol. Monogr.*, 20 (1950), 1-38.

Kimble, G. A., *Hilgard and Marquis Conditioning and Learning*. New York: Appleton-Century-Crofts, 1961.

Kornberg, A., "Biologic synthesis of deoxyribonucleic acids," *Science*, 131 (1960), 1503-8.

Krech, D., E. L. Bennett, and P. Ragan, "Effects of brain homogenate on reinstatement of early memory." Paper presented at AAAS symposium on Molecular Approaches to Learning and Memory, December, 1967.

Landauer, T. K., "Two hypotheses concerning the biochemical basis of memory," *Psychol. Rev.*, 71 (1964), 167-79.

Lashley, K. S., "In search of the engram," *Sympos. Soc. exp. Biol.*, 4 (1950), 454-82.

Lewis, S., "Maze acquisition and nucleic acid metabolism: effects of two malononitrile derivatives." Paper presented at Eastern Psychological Association Meetings, Boston, 1967.

Lubar, J. F., J. J. Boitano, E. M. Gurowitz, and B. R. Ain, "Enhancement of performance in the Hebb-Williams maze by magnesium pemoline," *Psychon. Sci.*, 7 (1967), 381-82.

Luttges, J., T. Johnson, C. Buck, J. Holland, and J. McGaugh, "An examination of 'transfer of learning' by nucleic acid," *Science,* 151 (1966), 834-37.

McConnell, J. V., "Memory transfer through cannibalism in planarians," *J. Neuropsychiat.,* 3 (1962), 42-48.

——, "On the turning of worms: a reply to James and Halas," *Psychol. Rec.,* 14 (1964), 13-20.

McConnell, J. V., A. L. Jacobson, and D. P. Kimble, "Effects of regeneration upon retention of a conditioned response in the planarian," *J. comp. physiol. Psychol.,* 52 (1959), 1-5.

McConnell, J. V., T. Shigehisha, and H. Salive, "Attempts to transfer approach and avoidance by RNA injections in rats." Paper presented at AAAS symposium on Molecular Approaches to Learning and Memory, December, 1967.

McLennan, H., *Synaptic Transmission.* Philadelphia: W. B. Saunders Co., 1963.

Madsen, M. C., and J. L. McGaugh, "Effect of ECS on one-trial avoidance learning," *J. comp. physiol. Psychol.,* 54 (1961), 522-23.

Mendelson, J., J. H. Mendelson, B. J. Fax, and R. G. Grenell, "Stability and absorption spectrum of malononitrile," *Science,* 120 (1954), 266-69.

Mihailović, Lj., B. D. Janković, M. Petković, and K. Isaković, "Effect of electroshock upon nucleic acid concentrations in various parts of cat brain," *Experientia,* 14 (1958), 144-45.

Morrell, F., "Lasting changes in synaptic organization produced by continuous neuronal bombardment," in *Brain Mechanisms and Learning,* ed. J. F. Delafresnaye. Springfield, Ill.: Charles C Thomas, Publisher, 1961.

Morris, N. R., G. K. Aghajanian, and F. E. Bloom, "Magnesium pemoline: failure to affect in vivo synthesis of brain RNA," *Science,* 155 (1967), 1125-26.

Nissen, Th., H. H. Roigaard-Petersen, and E. J. Fjerdingstad, "Effect of ribonucleic acid (RNA) extracted from the brain of trained animals on learning in rats. II: Dependence of RNA effect on training conditions prior to RNA extraction," *Scand. J. Psychol.,* 6 (1965), 265-72.

Ochs, S., *Elements of Neurophysiology.* New York: John Wiley & Sons, Inc., 1967.

Overton, R. K., "The calcium displacement hypothesis: a review," *Psychol. Rep.,* 5 (1959), 721-24.

Pearlman, C. A., S. K. Sharpless, and M. E. Jarvik, "Retrograde amnesia produced by anesthetic and convulsive agents," *J. comp. physiol. Psychol.,* 54 (1961), 109-12.

Pevzner, L. Z., "Nucleic acid changes during behavioral events," in *Macromolecules and Behavior,* ed. J. Gaito. New York: Appleton-Century-Crofts, 1966.

Plotnikoff, N., "Magnesium pemoline: enhancement of learning and memory of a conditioned avoidance response," *Science,* 151 (1966*a*), 703-4.

——, "Magnesium pemoline: enhancement of memory after electroconvulsive shock in rats," *Life Sciences,* 5 (1966*b*), 1495-98.

——, "Reply to Bowman," *Science,* 153 (1966*c*), 902.

Plotnikoff, N., and P. Meekma, Jr., "Pemoline and magnesium hydroxide versus pemoline: enhancement of learning and memory of a conditioned avoidance response in rats," *J. Pharmacol. Sci.,* 56 (1967), 290-91.

Reich, E., R. M. Franklin, A. T. Shotkin, and E. L. Tatum, "Action of actinomycin-D on animal cells and tissues," *Proc. Nat. Acad. Sci. (USA),* 48 (1962), 1238-45.

Revusky, S. H., and F. DeVenuto, "Attempt to transfer an aversion to saccharin solution by injection of RNA from trained to naïve rats." Paper presented at Psychonomic Society meetings, Chicago, October, 1967.

Rosenblatt, F., J. T. Farrow, and W. F. Herblin, "Transfer of conditioned responses from trained rats to untrained rats by means of a brain extract," *Nature,* 209 (1966), 46-48.

Rosenblatt, F., J. T. Farrow, and S. Rhine, "The transfer of learned behavior from trained to untrained rats by means of brain extracts. I, II." *Proc. Nat. Acad. Sci. (USA),* 55 (1966), 548-55, 787-92.

Rosenblatt, F., and R. G. Miller, "Behavioral assay procedures for transfer of learned behavior by brain extracts. I, II." *Proc. Nat. Acad. Sci. (USA),* 56 (1966), 1423-30.

Rosenthal, R., "On the social psychology of the psychology experiment: the experimenter's hypothesis as unintended determinant of the experimental results," *Amer. Scient.,* 51 (1963), 268-83.

Rosenthal, R., and E. S. Halas, "Experimenter effect in the study of invertebrate behavior," *Psychol. Rep.,* 11 (1962), 251-56.

Ruch, T. C., H. D. Patton, J. W. Woodbury, and A. L. Towe, *Neurophysiology.* Philadelphia: W. B. Saunders Co., 1965.

Rucker, W. B., and W. C. Halstead, "Memory: antagonistic transfer effects." Paper presented at AAAS Symposium on Molecular Approaches to Learning and Memory, December, 1967.

Schneider, A. M., "Control of memory by spreading depression: a case for stimulus control," *Psychol. Rev.,* 74 (1967), 201-15.

Smith, C. E., "Is memory a matter of enzyme induction?" *Science,* 138 (1962), 889-90.

Smith, R. G., "Magnesium pemoline: lack of facilitation in human learning, memory, and performance tests," *Science,* 155 (1967a), 603-5.

———, "Magnesium pemoline: lack of facilitation in human learning, memory, and performance tests." Paper presented at Eastern Psychological Association Meetings, Boston, 1967b.

Solyom, L., H. E. Enesco, and C. Beaulieu, "Effect of RNA on learning and activity in old and young rats," *J. Gerontol.,* 22 (1967), 1-7.

Solyom, L., and H. M. Gallay, "Effect of malononitrile dimer on operant and classical conditioning of aged white rats," *Internat. J. Neuropsychiat.,* 2 (1966), 577-84.

Talland, G. A., "Improvement of sustained attention with Cylert," *Psychon. Sci.,* 6 (1966), 493-94.

Thompson, R., and W. Dean, "A further study on the retroactive effect of ECS," *J. comp. physiol. Psychol.,* 48 (1955), 488-91.

Thompson, R., and J. V. McConnell, "Classical conditioning in the planarian *Dugesia dorotocephala,*" J. comp. physiol. Psychol., 48 (1955), 65-68.

Ungar, G., "Chemical transfer of learning: its stimulus specificity," *Fed. Proc.,* 25 (1966), 207 (Abstract).

——, "Transfer of learned information by brain extracts," *Fed. Proc.,* 26 (1967), 263 (Abstract).

Ungar, G., and L. N. Irwin, "Transfer of acquired information by brain extracts," *Nature,* 214 (1967), 453-55.

Ungar, G., and C. Oceguera-Navarro, "Transfer of habituation by material extracted from brain," *Nature,* 207 (1965), 301-2.

Vendrely, R., and C. Vendrely, "La teneur du noyau cellulaire en acide desoxyribonucleique à travers les organes, les individus, et les espèces animales," *Experientia,* 5 (1949), 327.

——, "The results of cytophotometry in the study of the deoxyribonucleic acid (DNA) content of the nucleus," *Internat. Rev. Cytol.,* 5 (1956), 171-97.

Vladimirov, G. E., T. N. Ivanov, and N. I. Pravdina, "Influence of the functional state on the metabolism of phosphorus compounds of brain tissue," *Biokhimiya,* 19 (1954), 578-85.

Wagner, A. R., J. B. Carder, and W. W. Beatty, "Yeast ribonucleic acid: effect on learned behavior in the rat," *Psychon. Sci.,* 4 (1966), 33-34.

Walker, D. R., "Memory transfer in planarians: an artifact of the experimental variables," *Psychon. Sci.,* 5 (1966), 357-58.

Walker, D. R., and G. A. Milton, "Memory transfer *vs.* sensitization in cannibal planarians," *Psychon. Sci.,* 5 (1966), 293-94.

Weiss, P., "The life history of the neuron," *Res. Publ. Ass. nerv. ment. Dis.,* 35 (1955), 8-18.

White, A., P. Handler, and E. L. Smith, *Principles of Biochemistry.* New York: McGraw-Hill Book Company, 1959.

Worthington, A. G., and M. B. Macmillan, "Maze preferences in naïve rats produced by injection of ribonucleic acid from trained rats: a further comment," *Psychon. Sci.,* 5 (1966), 298.

Yarmolinsky, M. B., and G. L. De La Haba, "Inhibition by puromycin of amino acid incorporation into protein," *Proc. Nat. Acad. Sci. (USA),* 45 (1959), 1721-29.

Yoshida, M., "Microspectrophotometric studies on deoxyribonucleic acid of an individual nucleus in the ox retina," *Jap. J. Physiol.,* 8 (1958), 57-66.

Zemp, J. W., J. E. Wilson, K. Schlesinger, W. O. Boggan, and E. Glassman, "Brain function and macromolecules, I: Incorporation of uridine into RNA of mouse brain during short-term training experience," *Proc. Nat. Acad. Sci. (USA),* 55 (1966), 1423-31.

INDEX

Subjects

Acetoxycycloheximide, 54-55, 57; effects on memory, 54-55
Acetylcholine, (ACh), 8, 47
Acetylcholinesterase, 8
Actinomycin-D, 30,32-34, 42; effects on metabolism, 32
Adenine, 15
Amino acids, 13
Anesthesia, effects on memory, 4-5
Arteriosclerosis, 37
ATP-role in protein synthesis, 21
Azaguanine, 30-32, 42; effects on metabolism, 50

Base changes, 29-30, 42
Base ratios, 16, 18
Bases, 15
Blood-brain barrier, 32, 41, 68

Calcium displacement hypothesis, 8
Cannibalism, 61-62
Conditioned emotional response, 3, 4, 5
Consolidation, 2
Convulsion, 26
Cortical spreading depression (CSD), 5, 72
CS-UCS interval, 44-45
Cytosine, 15

Deiter's nucleus, 29
Deoxyribonucleic acid (DNA): activation (derepression, 24, 48, 58; changes as result of behavior, 23; constancy theory, 23, 24; and nerve activity, 24; relationship to RNA, 18; stability and learning, 24; structure, 18-20
Drugs affecting memory (see also specific reference), 30-36, 50-56

Electroconvulsive shock (ECS), 1-4, 35, 51; effects on memory, 1-4; magnesium pemoline and, 35; punishment aspects of, 2ff; TCAP and, 50-51
Enzyme, 14
Enzyme induction, 22, 46, 47, 58
Escherichia coli, 18
Ethyl chloride, 27ff
Exhaustion, effect on RNA metabolism, 26
Experimenter bias, 61-62

Gamma-amino butyric acid, 8
Gene repression, 24, 48, 58
Genetic code, 7, 57
Glia, 29, 44
Guanine, 15

Habituation, 70
Hebb-Williams maze, 31, 32, 36, 40, 50f
Hydrogen bonding, 18
Hypothermia, 4f

Immune reaction, 75
Inhibition, 17f, 26, 42
Inter-animal transfer of learning, 59-76; and activity level, 71, 73, 75; blood-brain barrier and, 68; cerebellum and, 71; control problems, 74; cross-species, 65-66, 70, 74; experimenter bias in, 61-62; food ingestion and, 75; immune reactions and, 75; inversion effect, 72, 74; mammalian research, 65-70; non-RNA studies, 70-76; Planaria research, 59-64; protein in, 67-68, 70-71, 76; response specificity in, 70, 72, 75; RNA studies, 65-70; role

89

of RNA in, 67, 70-71, 76; sensitization and, 62ff, 66, 68, 73, 75; use of factorial design in, 69, 70, 74
Intra-animal transfer of learning, 60-61, 72-73

Learning set, 40-41

Magnesium pemoline, 30, 34-36, 42
Malnutrition, 37
Memory molecule, complex, 9, 24, 49, 77; criteria for, 8-9; Flexner, 57-58; Gaito, 24; Hydén, 43-44, 47-48; Katz and Halstead, 56-57; Landauer, 44-47; nature of, 7-9; theories of, Briggs and Kitto, 47
Methamphetamine, 34
Methylphenidate, 34
Metrazol, 4-5, 26, 27
Mirror focus, 27ff
Molar approaches to memory, 7-8
Molecular approaches to memory, 8-9
Molecular biology, 7
Mutation, genetic, 24

Narcotics, 23, 26
Neural circuits, 1, 8
Neural stimulation, effect on DNA, 23; effect on RNA, 25-26, 41-42, 47
Nucleic acids, 8-9, 14-17
Nucleoside, 16
Nucleotide, 16-17

Passive avoidance (PAR), 2ff, 5, 32-33, 34, 36
Pemoline, 34, 35
Peptides, 13
Planaria, 59-64, 75; "cannibalism experiments," 61-62; experimenter bias in work with, 61-62; learning in, 62-64
Polypeptides and memory, 67-68, 70, 71, 76
Primary structure, 16
Prosthetic group, 14
Protease, 14
Protein, 13ff, 21, 49-58; biosynthesis, 21; coding of amino acid sequence, 21; deprivation of, and learning, 56; drug studies, 32, 49-56
Pseudoconditioning, 62-64
Purine, 14, 15
Puromycin, 52-56, 57, 58
Pyrimidine, 14, 15

Regeneration, 60-61
Renshaw cell, 8
Retrograde amnesia, 3
Ribonuclease, 14
Ribonucleic acid, biosynthesis, 18; changes in learning, 26-30, 42, 46, 47; contamination, 65, 67-68, 71; drug studies, 30-36, 42; and inter-animal transfer, 65-70; metabolism, 18, 25-30, 41-42; and neural excitation, 25-26, 41-42, 47; and neural inhibition, 26-42; relationship to DNA, 18; yeast RNA, 34, 37-41, 42
Ribose, 15
RNA-DNA hybrid, 18

Secondary structure, 18
Senile dementia, 37
Sensitization, 62-63, 64, 66, 68, 73, 75
Spinal cord fixation, 31f, 50-51
Startle response, 70
Stimulant effects, in inter-animal transfer,
70, 75; magnesium pemoline, 35-36; yeast RNA, 38, 39, 40, 41, 42

TCAP, 30, 31, 49, 50-52, 56
T4CAP (see tetracyanoaminopropene)
Tertiary structure, 18
Tetracyanoaminopropene, 51
Thymine, 15

U-9189 (see TCAP)
Uracil, 15

Yeast RNA (see ribonucleic acid)

Names

Aghajanian, G. K., 36
Agranoff, B. W., 52
Ain, B. R., 36
Albert, D. J., 72
Alexander, M., 32
Andjus, R. K., 6

Babich, F. R., 65-68, 70, 71
Baggio, G. F., 26
Barik, H., 37
Barker, D. J., 67
Barondes, S. H., 32, 33, 41
Batkin, S., 33, 40
Beardsley, J., 68
Beatly, W. W., 38-39
Bloom, F. E., 36
Boggan, W. O., 58
Boitano, J. J., 36
Bowman, R., 35f
Bradfield, K., 68
Branch, J. C., 68
Briggs, M. H., 42, 47
Brodsky, V. Y., 23
Brown, H., 41
Brush, T. R., 51
Bubash, S., 65-68, 70, 71
Buck, C., 68
Bureš, J., 3, 5
Burešová, O., 3, 5
Byrne, W. L., 70, 72

Caldwell, D. F., 56
Cameron, D. E., 37-38
Carde, J. B., 38-39
Carey, F. M., 68
Carney, R. E., 66
Chamberlain, T. J., 31-32, 50, 51
Chapman, J. A., 35
Chitre, V. S., 26
Chopra, S. P., 26
Chorover, S. L., 3-4, 5
Churchill, J. A., 56
Cohen, S. D., 33, 41
Cole, R. E., 33, 40
Cook, L., 38-39, 41
Coons, E. E., 2
Cordaro, L., 62
Corning, W. C., 60-61, 62
Corson, J. A., 39-40, 67
Crick, F. H. C., 9, 19, 23

Davenport, J. W., 51
Davidson, A. B., 38-39, 41
Davis, D. J., 38-39, 41
Davis, R. E., 52

Dean, W., 2
DeBoer, M., 63
DeLa Haba, G., 52
Deutsch, D., 2
Deutsch, J. A., 2
Dingman, W., 9, 30, 31, 32
Duncan, C. P., 1-2
Dureman, E. T., 35
Dyal, J. A., 73

Eberts, F. S., 50
Egyházi, E., 29ff, 46, 50, 58
Eist, H., 41
Enesco, H. E., 38, 39-40, 67
Essman, W. B., 51, 68

Falbe-Hansen, J., 26
Farrow, J. T., 70-71
Fax, B. J., 50
Fellows, E. J., 38-39
Fjerdingstad, E. J., 65, 67, 74
Flexner, J. B., 47, 52, 53, 54, 55, 56, 57, 58
Flexner, L. B., 30, 47, 48, 52-56, 57-58
Franklin, R. M., 32
Fried, C., 64
Fruton, J. S., 14
Furth, T. T., 32

Gaito, J. A., 8, 9, 24, 46, 58
Gallay, H. M., 51
Gerard, R. W., 2, 4, 31-32, 50, 51
Glasky, A. J., 34f, 36
Glassman, E., 58
Goldberg, I. H., 32
Goldsmith, L. J., 34
Golub, A. M., 73
Gomirato, G., 26
Goren, C., 66-68
Green, H., 38-39,41
Grenell, R. B., 50
Gross, C., 68
Gross, D. A., 36, 75
Grossman, S. P., 2, 24, 46, 47, 56
Gurowitz, E. M., 36, 75

Halas, E. S., 61, 62-64, 68
Hall, J. B., 33, 40
Halstead, W. C., 8, 49, 50, 56-57
Hamberger, C.-A., 26
Handler, P., 13, 14, 15, 18, 21
Hartelius, H., 50
Hartry, A. L., 62, 63, 64
Hebb, D. O., 1, 8, 31, 32, 36, 40, 50
Herblin, W. F., 70-71
Holland, J., 68
Horowitz, S. D., 64
Hughes, A., 72
Hurwitz, J., 32
Hydén, H., 26, 28ff, 42-44, 47-48, 49-50, 58

Irwin, L. N., 70
Isaković, K., 23
Ison, J. R., 40, 42, 62
Ivanov, T. N., 23, 26

Jacobson, A., 65-68, 70, 71
Jacobson, A. L., 60, 64, 65-68, 70, 71
James, R. L., 62-64
Janković, B. D., 23
Jarvik, M. E., 4, 32, 34

John, E. R., 60-61, 62
Johnson, T., 68
Jones, J. E., 44

Karlson, P., 21, 22
Katz, J. J., 8, 49-50, 56-57
Keith-Lee, P., 62, 63, 64
Kimble, D. P., 60
Kimble, G. A., 63
Kitto, G. B., 42, 47
Knopfelmacher, F., 4
Knutson, C. S., 63
Kornberg, A., 24
Krech, D., 8, 47

Lahsley, K. S., 1
Landauer, T. K., 42, 44-47
Lange, P. W., 28ff, 46, 58
Lehrer, G. M., 48-69
Lewis, S., 51
Lubar, J. F., 36
Luttges, J., 68

McConnell, J. V., 59, 60, 61-62, 63-64
McGaugh, J., 2, 68
McLennan, H., 8
Macmillan, M. B., 67
Madsen, M. C., 2
Malamy, M., 32
Marrone, R. L., 73
Meekma, P., 35
Mendelson, J., 50
Mendelson, J. H., 50
Mihailović, Lj., 23
Miller, N. E., 2
Miller, R. G., 71-72, 74
Milton, G. A., 62
Morrell, F., 26ff
Morris, N. R., 36
Morton, W. D., 62, 63, 64
Moyer, K. E. 35
Müller, G. E., 2
Mulry, R. C., 63

Nissen, Th., 65, 67, 74

Oceguera-Navarro, C., 70, 71, 75
Ochs, S., 8, 45
Overton, R. K., 8

Pakkenberg, H., 26
Patton, H. D., 8
Pavlov, I. P., 8
Pearlman, C. A., 4
Petković, M., 23
Pevzner, L. Z., 25, 26
Pigon, A., 29
Pilzecker, A., 2
Plotnikoff, N., 34ff
Polidora, V. J., 51
Pravdina, N. I., 23, 26

Rabinowitz, M., 32
Reich, E., 32
Rhine, S., 71
Roberts, R. B., 47, 52, 54, 55, 58
Røigaard-Petersen, H. H., 65, 67, 74
Rosenblatt, F., 70-72, 74
Rosenthal, R., 61-62
Rothschild, G. H., 31-32, 50,51
Ruch, T. C., 8
Russell, R. W., 4

Samuel, D., 72
Sandlie, M. E., 68
Schiller, P. H., 3-4, 5
Schlesinger, K., 58
Schneider, A. M., 5
Seal, U. S., 41
Sharpless, S. K., 4
Shotkin, A. T., 32
Simmonds, S., 14
Simon, L. N., 34f, 36
Smith, A. U., 4
Smith, C. E., 47
Smith, E. L., 13, 14, 15, 18
Smith, R. G., 35-36
Solyom, L., 37, 38, 41, 51
Sporn, M. B., 9, 30-31, 32
Stellar, E., 52, 53
Stone, L. A., 62-63
Sved, S., 37

Talland, G. A., 35, 36
Talwar, G. P., 26
Taplin, P., 40, 42
Tatum, E. L., 32
Theye, F., 68
Thompson, R., 2, 63

Towe, A. L., 8

Ungar, G., 70, 71, 75

Vendrely, C., 23
Vendrely, R., 23
Viney, W., 68
Vladimirov, G. E., 23, 26

Wagner, A. R., 38-39
Wainrib, B., 37
Walker, D. R., 62
Watson, J. D., 19
Weiss, P., 44
White, A., 13, 14, 15, 18
Williams, K., 31, 32, 36, 40, 50
Wilson, J. E., 58
Woodbury, J. W., 8
Woodward, W. T., 33, 40
Worthington, A. G., 67

Yarmolinsky, M. B., 52
Yoshida, M., 24

Zavala, A., 8
Zemp, J. W., 58